# A Kind of
Homecoming

**Eugene McEldowney**

# A Kind of
# Homecoming

St. Martin's Press
New York

A KIND OF HOMECOMING. Copyright © 1994 by Eugene McEldowney.
All rights reserved. Printed in the United States of America. No
part of this book may be used or reproduced in any manner
whatsoever without written permission except in the case of
brief quotations embodied in critical articles or reviews. For
information, address St. Martin's Press, 175 Fifth Avenue,
New York, N.Y. 10010.

Library of Congress Cataloging-in-Publication Data

McEldowney, Eugene.
    A kind of homecoming / Eugene McEldowney.
        p.   cm.
    ISBN 0-312-11016-2
    1. Police—Northern Ireland—Fiction.   I. Title.
    PR6063.C396K56   1994
    823'.914—dc20                                      94-6396
                                                        CIP

First published in Great Britain by William Heinemann Ltd.

First U.S. Edition August 1994
10  9  8  7  6  5  4  3  2  1

For Maura

# A Kind of
Homecoming

# 1

Stewart turned instinctively when he heard the sound, a rustling in the long grass, about half-way down the field. He stopped and a cry surprised him. All at once he saw a pheasant start up from the ground, flapping its wings in furious warning.

He watched as it flew into the sky which was beginning to brighten now above Glencraigie Hill. For a moment the bird seemed to hang in the air, a brilliant ball of bronze and gold. Then it was swooping low over the meadow and the sound of its wings was like breath against his face. He watched till it was lost from sight beyond the trees.

Stewart started walking again, briskly this time as if he was late for an appointment. He knew what the bird meant. It was an omen. It meant good luck. As he rounded a bend in the road, he saw the car.

It was an old Ford Cortina and it was parked at an awkward angle, with its wheels up against the grass verge. Inside he could see a figure, a man waiting patiently in the driving seat. Stewart hurried forward, his rough workman's boots clitter-clattering on the dusty road and the sound echoing across the empty fields.

As he drew near, he saw that the man was asleep, his body slumped forward across the steering wheel. Stewart bent to peer through the window. The man's arms were drawn up above his shoulders. There was a sack covering his head. Then he saw the blood. It had soaked the man's coat and shirt and was forming a thick gelatinous pool around the floor.

Stewart felt afraid. He turned from the car and began to run, back along the way he had come. He thought he heard a sound, a sharp click like a bolt being withdrawn from a lock. The first bullet caught him on the side of the mouth.

His face exploded in pain. He started to cry out and then there was a roar like a car exhaust and the road was filled with noise. A second bullet struck his shoulder and spun him round. There was another and another, each one lifting him off the ground in a crazy dance.

He began to fall as the power drained from his legs. He could hear voices, the sound of running feet. One more shot hit his chest and kicked him backwards into the ditch.

Through a bloody mist, he could see the sun coming up over Glencraigie Hill. His breath was leaving him. He closed his eyes and there it was. The bird was dancing again, hovering against the light, blinding him with its bright colours.

# 2

The phone on Megarry's desk rang. For a second he watched it, mesmerised by the sound. Then he reached out an unsteady hand to silence it.

Nelson got there first. He held the instrument close to his mouth and spoke down the line. 'Detective unit.'

'Is he there?' a voice asked.

Nelson looked across to the police chief. He had his cigarettes out and was frantically shaking his head.

'He's busy right now,' Nelson said. 'Can I help?'

'Don't give me that bullshit,' the voice said. 'I know he's there. Tell him this is important. I've got two stiffs on a road out by Glencraigie. Gunshot wounds.'

Nelson quickly cupped his hand over the mouthpiece and whispered across the desk. 'It's Harvey. There's been a shooting.'

'Jeeesus,' Megarry said. 'That's all I need.'

He grabbed the phone.

'What happened, Fred?'

'Two men dead. The reports are just coming in.'

'Any of our people?'

'I'm not sure. It's all very confused.'

'Who's out there?'

'Just the local cops. An Inspector Blair rang in on the car phone. One of these guys is badly cut up.'

'How bad?'

'He's mangled, Cecil.'

Megarry swore under his breath. 'Get on to the Press Office. Tell them I want a blackout. Tell them nothing's to get out till we've had a chance to study this. I don't want reporters crawling all over the place.'

'Do you want somebody to go out?'

'No. I'll look after it. Tell them I'm on my way.'

He was about to put the phone down when something else occurred to him.

'When did this happen?'

'I just told you, Cecil. It's all very vague. The postman reported it shortly after nine.'

'All right. Calm down. Don't get excited.'

'You calm down!' Harvey shouted. 'I'm here on my own. What do you expect me to do? Go out there and investigate? I'm only monitoring reports, for Christ's sake.'

Megarry banged the phone down. He glanced at his watch. It was twenty to ten. He tapped ash from his cigarette and tried to control the tremor in his hand.

'Can I do anything?' Nelson asked.

Megarry turned to observe the younger man. He was sitting across the desk with a coffee cup in his hand. Healthy, fit, bursting with energy. Once I looked like that, he thought. But it was a long time ago. Before they began to grind me down.

'No. It's all right. I need time to think.'

He bent and pulled out a drawer, his heavy belly straining against his shirt.

'Maybe you should get something to eat?' Nelson said cautiously. 'I can go to the canteen.'

Megarry shook his grey face. He had a small square of toilet paper stuck to his chin where he had nicked himself shaving.

'I know what I need.'

Under a pile of folders he found what he was looking for. A bottle of Black Bush, kept for emergencies. His trembling hands unscrewed the cap and poured the whiskey into a coffee mug. He held out the bottle but Nelson waved it away.

'Too early.'

The police chief grunted and poured another measure. He waited while the whiskey burned its way down into his gut, then wiped his mouth with the back of his hand.

'We'll have to go out there.'

'I'll drive.'

'Why does this have to happen, John? This morning of all mornings. I'm not half awake yet. Jesus Christ.'

He began vigorously massaging his temples with his knotted fists.

'You'll be all right,' Nelson said. 'The fresh air will do you good.'

'What time did I get home?'

'Three o'clock.'

Megarry tried to count. 'Did I do anything daft? Insult anybody? Make a show of myself?'

Nelson was smiling. 'Nothing like that. You were fine.'

'You're being diplomatic.'

'No, I'm not. You walked out of the Montrose straight as an arrow.'

'It must have been a miracle. I don't even remember. What did we talk about?'

'Office politics, mainly. You were bitching.'

'What'd I do? Fall asleep?'

'You were tired, that's all.'

Megarry sighed. 'It was meant to be only a couple of drinks. Just to unwind.'

'You've been working too hard.'

'Wellll.' He suddenly changed the subject. 'Any calls?'

Nelson consulted a notepad.

'Nothing urgent. Guy called Smith rang from the Northern Ireland office to remind you about tomorrow's security meeting.'

'Anything else?'

'Your wife called.'

'Oh.' Megarry put down his mug. 'What time?'

'Half nine.'

'Any message?'

'No. I told her you hadn't come in yet. She said she'd ring again.'

'We'd better go,' Megarry said.

He stood up and lifted his coat. The phone rang. In an instant, Nelson had it tight against his ear. Megarry watched him shake his head.

'He's not here.'

There was a crackle on the line.

'I know nothing about it. You'll have to go through the Press Office.'

He put the instrument down and looked up.

'The BBC. About Glencraigie. They're looking for a statement.'

'Whaaat? I told Harvey to issue a blackout. How the hell did they find out?'

The phone rang again. This time Megarry grabbed it.

'We got cut off,' a voice said.

'I know what I'll cut off.'

'I beg your pardon?'

'You heard me.'

'I don't like your attitude.'

'I don't give a shit what you like. Where did you get this number?'

'Now, just a minute.'

'No. You just a minute. I'm a very busy man. I don't have time to talk to you. And furthermore. This is a private line. The next time you use it, I'll personally have you done for breaching the Official Secrets Act. Is that clear?'

'I'm only doing my job.'

Megarry slammed the phone down. 'Jeeesus,' he said. His face had gone deep crimson. 'Where did he get that number?'

'Search me,' Nelson said.

Megarry had his coat on and was pulling open the door.

'Well, get it changed. What's this place coming to? Where's the godammed security? We can't have people ringing the detective unit like it was the godammed speaking clock.'

# 3

Above Ligoniel they left the main traffic behind. The road climbed steeply and then they were in open countryside, cows lazing in the morning sun, byres, sheds, tractors. The rich smell of farm manure hung in the air. Megarry closed the window and lit a cigarette.

'You know where you're going?'

Nelson kept his eyes on the road. 'Sort of.'

'Clady Corner. Then the Seven Mile Straight. You can't miss it.'

The other man said nothing. Megarry shifted in his seat and stretched his legs. 'I know this place. Nice quiet country town. I used to come here to bowling tournaments with my old man. He was a champion bowler. Did I ever tell you that?'

'I think you did.'

'He loved bowling. He used to live for it. We travelled half the country together when I was your age.' He stopped to see how Nelson was reacting. 'It's a very skillful game.

Requires concentration, a good eye. And stamina. You'd be amazed.'

'Sounds interesting.'

'You have to be fit.'

'Sure.'

Megarry suddenly leaned forward. 'You think I'm kidding? You think it's a game for geriatrics? Old men in blazers and white flannels. You think I'm making this up?'

'I didn't say a word,' Nelson protested and smiled innocently.

'No? But I know what you're thinking. You don't have to say it.' He stubbed the cigarette out and sat back in his seat. After a while he spoke again.

'What did Kathleen say?'

'I told you. She just asked for you and I said you hadn't come in.'

'And that's all? She didn't ask where I was, how I was keeping? No chit-chat. Just wham, bam and thank you ma'am?'

'That's all,' Nelson said. He turned to face the older man.

'And how did she sound?'

'She sounded fine.'

'Just "fine"?'

'Hey, I was only talking to her for thirty seconds.'

Megarry sniffed and turned back to the window. The countryside was flashing past in the bright sunshine. They were travelling along a narrow road, the ditches lined with hawthorn in white blossom. Around them the fields stretched flat as a hand. Away in the distance he could see a steeple, smoke rising from the chimneys of a town.

After a while they came to a crossroads and a black and white signpost said Glencraigie. A few miles further on they saw the first cars. Megarry leaned forward and pointed.

'Over there. Pull in.'

He untangled his seat belt and waited for Nelson to stop. Ahead on the road there was a police barrier and flashing lights. Someone had stuck up a diversion sign.

As Megarry got out, a small man in a tweed jacket turned and saw him. He pushed through the mill of police officers and strode across.

'Superintendent,' he said. 'Good to see you. Nasty business, this.' He made a tutting noise with his mouth.

Megarry nodded and turned to Nelson. 'You know my colleague, John Nelson. Dr Ryder.'

The small man smiled at Nelson. 'I think we met before,' he said. He stuck out a chubby hand. Nelson noticed the bloodstains. 'You'll have to forgive me. I haven't had a chance to wash.'

Megarry said, 'What's it looking like?'

The small man took his glasses off and began to polish them with a handkerchief. He seemed to be enjoying the excitement. 'I'm not sure. There's something odd. Something not right.'

'Like what?'

The doctor took Megarry by the elbow and drew him aside. He lowered his voice. 'One of these men has half his head blown away. The man in the ditch.' He pointed to a tarpaulin with white chalk marks around it. 'The man in the car doesn't even look as if he's dead.' His cheeks spread in a playful smile. 'Once you discount the bag and the brains, that is. He had a bag around his head. A sort of potato sack. But you get my point. The features are still intact.'

Megarry stared at him. The small man smiled again.

'Oh, he's dead all right. He was shot in the neck.' He put his glasses back on and pointed a pudgy finger below his left ear. 'Here. Neat entrance wound. Large exit at the top of the skull. Death due to brain haemorrhage, I'd say. But that's only preliminary. I'll have to get them down to the morgue for a proper autopsy.'

'What are you trying to tell me?'

The small man shrugged. 'Different weapons. The poor devil in the road is a mess. They blew half his head away. Looks to me like an automatic rifle. And he has wounds to the spine, chest and abdomen. I can only find one wound on the man in the car.' He paused and lowered his voice again. 'Like he was executed.'

Megarry turned away. He looked back. A couple of men were down on their hands and knees combing the gravel of the roadway. 'Who's in charge of forensics?'

'They've gone,' the small man said. 'Inspector Robinson. Those men are only mopping up.'

'Did they find anything?'

'I'm not sure. I was too busy with my own work.'

The doctor stood for a moment in silence, his hands dug deep in his pockets. 'Do you want to have a look? I should warn you. It's not pleasant.'

A red-faced RUC man saluted and stood aside to let them pass. Dr Ryder bent down and drew away the heavy cloth.

A thin man, about fifty, lay on his back, an unseeing eye gazing into the sun. He was dressed in rough labourer's clothes. His face and head were a mangled mess, features barely distinguishable, as if someone had taken a knife, and cut and hacked at the dark red flesh.

Megarry felt his stomach gag. He stood up quickly.

'The other one's not as bad,' the small man said.

'Do we know who they are?'

'Not yet.'

The doctor walked across to the battered Ford Cortina and began to pull open the door. Immediately a sickly warm smell reached them. Inside a man lay slumped over the steering wheel in drunken repose, arms stretched above his head. His neck and shoulders were drenched in blood. From the side of his skull a mass of white brain oozed from a gaping wound, blue veins dappling the membrane like marble.

Megarry reached out and touched the man's shoulder. The head suddenly rolled back into the seat and the jaw fell open, glazed eyes staring lifeless in the grey face.

For a moment Megarry felt his heart stop. 'Jesus,' he muttered. He stepped back quickly from the car and breathed in the fresh air.

'Superintendent,' a voice said.

Megarry turned to find a tall man in a white gaberdine standing beside him. His handsome face was wrinkled into a serious frown. From behind, the sun came filtering through the fine hairs on the crown of his head.

'Ghastly business.'

Megarry felt confused.

'You look pale,' the man said. 'Are you all right?' He held out his hand and the policeman took it.

'I'm fine. Just the shock.'

Megarry saw his nostrils twitch. Had he smelt the whiskey on his breath?

'I heard about this at HQ,' the man said. 'Your local chap alerted us. I thought I'd better come over and see for myself. It looks pretty grim. Paramilitaries, I suppose?'

Megarry took a deep breath and searched for his cigarettes. 'I suppose so. I don't know.' He turned to the doctor. 'Where's the ambulance?'

The small man looked at his watch. 'I rang twenty minutes ago. Maybe I should call again. Excuse me.'

He walked quickly towards the line of police cars. The tall man watched him depart. He turned back to Megarry.

'Have we identified them?'

'Not yet.'

'Security personnel?'

'I don't think so.'

'And nobody's claimed responsibility?'

'No,' Megarry said. 'It's too early.'

The man put a hand to his mouth and cleared his throat. 'I never get used to it. Seeing people get killed. I know that sounds odd, but I find it unsettling. It's not like a real war where you expect casualties.'

Megarry was looking around anxiously for Nelson.

'This place is so peaceful. Lovely countryside. It all seems so out of place.' He gestured towards the fields stretching away to Glencraigie Hill. Beyond a belt of trees they could see the flash of water on a lake.

'Major, I'll have to go.'

'I'll see you tomorrow.'

The police chief suddenly remembered. 'Of course, the security meeting.'

'Any developments, let me know. I like to be kept informed.'

Nelson detached himself from a knot of uniformed men and they began to walk back towards their car. At the barriers a posse of reporters had gathered, notebooks at the ready. Megarry saw a television camera poking above their heads.

'What can you tell us?' A man in a grey suit pushed his way forward. He tried to block the policemens' path.

'No comment,' Megarry said. He started to elbow his

way through the throng. Suddenly he stopped and turned back to face them. 'Which of you guys is from the BBC?'

A young man with thick horn-rimmed glasses waved a microphone in recognition.

Megarry dived through the crowd and grabbed him by the lapels. 'Did you ring me this morning?'

The man tried to protect his glasses. 'No,' he said. 'Not me.'

'You're sure?'

'Positive.'

The police chief shoved him away. 'One of your colleagues did. On a private line. You tell him from me, if he does that again, I'll personally break his legs.' He pushed past the remaining reporters, scattering them out of his way.

'What was all that about?' the man in the grey suit said. He started to shout after the retreating policemen. 'Hey, you can't behave like that. Who do you think you are?'

A few heads began to turn. Megarry ignored them, pushing forward through the throng.

'You can't do that,' the man in the grey suit was shouting.

Megarry reached the car and settled into the passenger seat.

'Calm down,' Nelson said. 'Take it easy.'

Megarry opened his mouth and then closed it again. 'Just drive,' he said.

'I don't think you should have done that,' Nelson said as they settled into the car.

'Done what?'

'Roughed that guy up.'

Megarry stared. 'What are you talking about? I hardly touched him.'

'You pulled him by the lapels.'

'That's nothing.'

'It's enough for him to lodge an official complaint. You know what they're like. And he'd loads of witnesses.'

'He had our private number. Now where do you think he got that? Somebody must have given it to him. That means a handful of people.'

'Nevertheless. Don't give them ammunition.'

'C'mon.'

'I'm telling you. Give them half a chance and they'll be screaming about police brutality.'

'Just a minute,' Megarry said. He unbuckled his seat belt. 'How old are you now?'

'Twenty-six.'

'You're twenty-six.' He rubbed his chin. 'Well, let me tell you something. When I was twenty-six, I was walking the toughest parts of the city. On my own a lot of the time. The docks, the markets, the Falls. When the hard men saw me coming, they would run. Nowadays we can't get guys to go into those districts unless they're in a car.'

'What's that got to do with anything?'

'It's got everything to do with it. Do you think those guys were afraid of me because I went around with kid gloves? You bet your sweet life they weren't. They were afraid because I didn't take any cheek. Because I'd think nothing of kicking their arses, or worse. I put manners on them and they respected me for it.' He sniffed. 'And you know what? I never got one complaint. Not one. So don't talk to me about roughing people up.'

He put his seat belt back on and stared out of the window. Nelson ignited the engine and said no more.

After a while Nelson made a couple of efforts to engage

Megarry, but they came to nothing. A stony silence settled over the car.

On the outskirts of Templepatrick Megarry came alive. He stirred in his seat and turned to the detective.

'There's a pub here. Near the top of Main Street. Why don't we stop and have something to eat?'

They watched for the sign. It was a spirit grocery: half pub, half village shop. 'McQuillan', it said in faded letters above the window. Nelson pulled the car across the road and parked outside the locked gates of the Presbyterian Church.

A bell rang as they pushed the door open and a faint odour of stale beer and polish met them. A massive cat lay stretched in the window, sleeping in the sun. At the sound of the bell, a boy in a white shirt peeped up from behind the counter.

'Do you do lunches?' Megarry asked.

From the back of the house an older voice sounded. 'Who is it, Michael?'

'Just a couple of customers. I can look after them.' He turned back again to the policemen. 'Not cooked lunches. I could get you soup and sandwiches.'

'What have you got?'

'Ham, cheese, salad.'

'I'll have a bowl of soup and a ham sandwich.'

He looked to Nelson for confirmation but Nelson was already nodding.

'Make that double. And two pints of stout. Can you manage that?'

'Yes, sir,' the boy said eagerly and immediately started reaching for glasses.

Megarry turned and looked around the pub. It was empty.

Above the fireplace an old-fashioned sign showed a woman in 1920's dress leaning on the bonnet of a car and smoking a cigarette. Gold Flake, it said. At the back of the room he could see mirrors and harness bells and something that looked like a cart wheel leaning against a wall. He walked to the window and sat down at a table.

Nelson joined him. 'Feeling better?'

'I'll survive.'

'You look woozy.'

'I had a shock back there. Did you see that guy?'

'The one in the car?'

Megarry lowered his eyes. 'I think I recognised him.'

'What?'

A movement interrupted them and the boy set down two black pints of Guinness. He looked even younger now that he was out from behind the counter, a schoolboy probably, working his holidays. His shirt sleeves were rolled up to the elbows, skinny white arms drooping like poles. 'I'll have the food right away.' He hovered for a moment and then disappeared back towards the bar.

Megarry reached for his pint. Nelson held his arm.

'What did you say?'

'I think I recognised the man in the car.'

'You knew him?'

'I think so. It's a long time ago.' He took a pull from the glass and wiped his chin. 'I haven't seen him for fifteen, maybe twenty years. I could be wrong. It may not be him at all.' He put the glass down. 'He looked awful. His brains were hanging out like a balloon. And the smell in that car. Jesus.' He screwed his face up.

'Who was he?'

'A guy called John McCarthy. He was an informer. I met him first when I was just starting out. He used to work for me. He was the best in town. He delivered . . .' He stopped and spread his hands. 'I don't know. Maybe half the IRA in Belfast. Arms dumps, safe houses, personnel. Big fish, people on their command structure. Between us, we put them out of business for a long time. I had to lean on him at first but he got to like it in the end.' He had lowered his voice as if he was talking about an old friend.

'How did you lose touch?'

'I had to let him go. He was too good. Made himself redundant. He'd nothing more to offer. I know that sounds callous, but I couldn't keep on paying him when he wasn't bringing in the dope.'

'Was he still at the old business?'

'Could be. But if he was, he wasn't working for me.'

The boy was back with a tray loaded with soup and sandwiches, cutlery and napkins. He set them down proudly and then stood up. 'Will that be all, sir?'

'I'll have another pint,' Megarry said. He glanced towards Nelson but the detective was shaking his head.

'Just one. And you can bring me the bill.' He lifted a spoon and dipped into the soup.

Near the window a bluebottle buzzed intermittently, hurling itself against the pane, confused by the glass. The sound had woken the cat and it watched with a lazy eye, trying to summon the energy to strike. The talk about Glencraigie seemed to have quietened Megarry again. After a while, Nelson tried to revive the conversation.

'So what do we do now?'

'Wait for the autopsy and the forensic report. I'll go and see Ryder this afternoon. In the meantime you keep the meddlers at bay. Just tell them I'm not available.' He reached for a sandwich and bit into the crisp ham, pulling off pieces of fat that hung like white skin from the bread.

'I can't stand interference. All those busybodies. They think they know my job better than I do. Just keep them off my back.'

He lapsed into silence again. Nelson became aware of the loud ticking of a clock above the fireplace. Behind the bar, the boy was rinsing glasses, carefully polishing them with a white cloth.

Eventually, Megarry drained his pint and stood up. 'We'd better go.' At the counter he paid the bill.

As they walked towards the car, he took Nelson's arm.

'I was thinking. He must have a wife and family. People who love him. People who'll grieve now that he's gone.'

'Who?'

'McCarthy.'

'Probably,' Nelson said. 'It's not our concern.'

'But I got him involved in this racket. I brought him into it.'

He said no more till they were back in the car and then turned again to the detective. 'I owe him a lot, you know.'

'But you're not even sure it's him.'

Megarry blinked for a moment in the glare from the windscreen. 'You're right. It could be someone else. His face was a mess. I won't know for certain till I've seen him in the morgue. Still . . .' He paused as if turning something over in his head. 'To end up like that.'

Harvey's office was a cramped box with peeling paint and no windows, squeezed beside the lift-shaft and the canteen. A smell of cooking seemed to pervade every crack. He sat like a prisoner behind a battered desk with three phones and a pile of papers, the light from the single bulb dancing off his head. He looked up when Megarry pushed the door open.

'I've just got it,' he said. 'Don't say another word.'

He ran a palm across his chin and dived into a heap of files, pulling out envelopes and folders. He stopped and gave the police chief a harassed look.

'It's here somewhere. I had it a few minutes ago.'

'Take your time,' Megarry said.

He pulled over a chair and waited while Harvey rummaged among the litter on his desk. At last he gave a whoop and extracted a thin blue file. He pushed it across. 'It's just come in. Here. You read it.'

One of the phones rang. 'Excuse me,' Harvey said. He lifted the instrument. 'Control.'

Megarry opened the file and started to read. The typing was erratic, banged out on a faulty machine with the letter 't' unaligned so that it stuck up above the rest of the line. PRELIMINARY FORENSIC REPORT, it said. Megarry's eye travelled down the page.

Incident reported by local postman, Mr C. Watson at 9am, June 8th.

He knew that already.

Man in the road suffered fifteen gunshot wounds to head, spine, chest and abdomen. Automatic rifle fire from two separate weapons. Likely cause of death, brain haemorrhage, heart failure.

Man in car suffered single bullet wound to head from Browning pistol. Likely cause of death, brain haemorrhage. Car stolen in West Belfast. Owner reported theft on June 5th. Fingerprints match owner and deceased person.

The report continued with details of cartridge shells recovered, items found on bodies of deceased, fibre samples sent for analysis. At the bottom a scrawled signature read: R. Donaldson.

Megarry put the file back on the desk. 'Who's Donaldson?'

Harvey looked up from the phone. 'He's our forensic man.'

'Have you read this?'

'I've glanced through it.'

'What do you make of it?'

Harvey shrugged. 'It's a mess.'

'Different weapons,' Megarry said. 'And a Browning pistol. That's odd, surely.'

Harvey spread his hands. 'There's loads of them around. They're getting stolen all the time.'

'But why the different weapons? And the ferocity of it. That poor guy in the ditch was nearly cut to pieces. Fifteen fucking bullets. I had a look at him. His face was mangled. He didn't know what hit him.'

Harvey sniffed and loosened his tie. 'You're looking for logic in it. There's no logic in it. These people are just animals. They don't care what they do.'

'What about a motive? It wasn't robbery. The man in the car had eighty pounds in his wallet according to this.' He tapped the file on the desk.

Harvey raised his sad eyes and sighed. 'Who needs a motive anymore?'

'What about the car owner? Anybody talked to him?'

'There's somebody with him now. He's looking clean. He reported the car as soon as he found it missing. Three friggin' days ago.'

'Any identification?'

Harvey reached into the pile of folders and pulled out a sheet of paper. 'Here,' he said. 'The man in the road was David Stewart. Farm labourer. Local man. No criminal record. The other guy was John McCarthy. He's from West Belfast. Unemployed. String of convictions for petty crime. Same age, fifty-two. But.' He raised a finger. 'Different religions.'

Megarry took the paper. 'You think that's significant?'

'Could be.'

Megarry glanced quickly at the second name and gave the paper back. 'We're sure of these?'

'They've been confirmed.'

'How did we identify the man in the car?'

'He had a social welfare card in his wallet. Along with the money.'

'Anything else?'

'Just the usual. Bits and pieces. Blood donor card. Yeah he was a blood donor. That's ironic, don't you think?' He spread his face in a grin. The police chief ignored the remark.

'Anybody identify the bodies? Next of kin?'

'I don't think so,' Harvey said. He turned his head back to the desk and started rummaging again. After a while he looked up. 'No. I've nothing about that. It's too early.'

Megarry stood up from the chair. 'Can we keep it like that? Just for a while?'

Harvey immediately looked worried. 'It's unusual.'

'I need time. I don't want it all over the papers. Somebody blabbed about the incident this morning. The place was crawling with reporters. They get in the way.'

'Forty-eight hours is about all we can manage. After that you're asking for trouble. They'll have their solicitors on to us.'

'Forty-eight hours is fine. Just say nothing till I get back to you. If there's any problem, I'll take responsibility.'

Harvey sighed. 'All right,' he said.

At the door, Megarry turned again. 'Are you happy here?'

'In the RUC?'

'No, in this little hole. Don't you ever get fed up with no light and the smell of boiled cabbage all day long. This place stinks.'

The phone rang again. 'I know. What can I do?'

Megarry shrugged. 'Nothing, I suppose.'

Megarry pulled the car close into the kerb and knocked the engine off. He sat for a moment and let his eyes sweep the street from left to right. He was beginning to unhook his seat belt when a blue Volvo pulled in, a business man in a dark suit confident at the wheel. The police chief stopped and waited.

Across the road the two-storey building sat like a giant packing case, the paint peeling from the windows, graffiti scarred across its black walls. He could already feel the chill. It was always the same. He had grown to hate the place.

The business man had found a parking space and was starting to reverse. Megarry watched him wrestle with the wheel, spinning it frantically with both hands, silent expletives tumbling from his lips. The police chief checked the rear mirror again and stepped out into the dying sunshine.

A few blocks away he could hear the drone of traffic, the tail end of the rush hour. But here it was quiet. Nothing but parked cars. A man with a dog was strolling at the end of the street. Megarry bent quickly to lock the door and instinctively looked about once more. Satisfied, he skipped across the road and ran up the steps into the gloomy interior of the morgue.

Just inside the glass doors an important little man in

a scuffed uniform sat behind a security desk. He looked up when he saw the policeman and immediately busied himself to be helpful.

'Superintendent? What can I do for you?'

He started to get up out of his chair, civil service issue with the formica peeling from the back.

'I'm here to see Dr Ryder.'

'Dr Ryder, is it? Right away.'

He reached for a console on his desk and began punching buttons.

'Is Dr Ryder there? Would you tell him I've Superintendent Megarry here waiting for him.' He held the phone pressed tight against his ear and nodded across the desk as he spoke. 'Yes. He's expecting him. Right away. Very good.' He put the phone back and straightened himself up. 'He'll be with you in a minute, superintendent. Why don't you take a seat?'

He pulled a second chair out from behind the desk. Megarry studied him. Ferrety type with a nervous tic under his left eye. Ex sergeant-major probably, stuck in here in a nice pensionable job after he'd retired. The little man was speaking again in an exaggerated accent.

'Is it them fellas was brought in this morning from Glencraigie?' The tic was pulsating and Megarry got a weird impression that the eye might suddenly jump out of its socket. 'Terrible business. When's it all going to end, superintendent?' He poked a finger into the policeman's chest. 'Do you know what it is? We're far too soft with them. That's the trouble. They know they can get away with it.'

He waited for the police chief's reaction but Megarry ignored him so he gripped his lapels and sat down again.

'There was none of this carry-on when we had the

death penalty. They're not afraid, you see. And when they get caught they get the kid glove treatment. These prisons are a joke. They're like holiday camps. Best of everything. Sure these guys are better looked after than you or me.'

Megarry let him ramble on. He was fed up listening to these conversations. Everybody seemed to have instant solutions. It wasn't that simple. After a while the man changed direction.

'That's a grand bit of weather we're getting, all the same.' He leaned his elbows on the desk and stared out onto the street where the dying sun was casting shadows on the road. 'Good gardening weather. Do you ever have time for the garden, superintendent?'

Megarry opened his mouth to speak, but there was a sound of footsteps and a door was flung open. Ryder came bustling across the hall. He wore a white doctor's coat and brought with him a smell of disinfectant. He stretched out his chubby little hand in welcome.

'I have him ready. Cleaned him up. You won't recognise him.' He stopped and grinned. 'What am I saying? Of course you will. The whole idea is that you should recognise him. Isn't that right? That's why you're here.' He gave a little gurgle. 'Well, let's see. Let's see. Come this way.'

He took Megarry's arm and steered him along a corridor, painted in depressing grey.

'Have you completed the autopsy?'

Ryder nodded. 'Haemorrhage of the brain, like I said. Entrance wound beneath left ear. Exit wound at back of the skull. Of course, there'll have to be an inquest.'

He stopped in front of a metal door and pulled out a bunch of keys. 'And here's another odd thing. He was killed at least four hours before the other man.'

Megarry caught his breath. 'What did you say?'

'Allowing an hour for margin of error. I can't be specific.'

He pushed the door open and Megarry immediately felt the chill from the refrigerated room. The police chief put a hand on the doctor's chest.

'Let's get this straight. This man was murdered four hours before the man on the road?'

'Maybe five,' Ryder said. 'The man on the road. What's his name, Stewart, was shot around five o'clock this morning. This man was shot much earlier. About midnight or one o'clock, I'd say.'

He paused before a bank of steel cabinets and checked the names, then gripped the handle and pulled. There was a grating sound as the trolley rolled out from the wall on its aluminium wheels. Wrapped in a white linen sheet, there was the clear outline of body.

'This is our man,' Ryder said. He reached over quickly and pulled the sheet away to reveal a grey torso underneath. Except for the deathly pallor it could have been a patient prepared for an operation.

Megarry swallowed hard.

The body had been washed, but here and there on the pale forehead a few specks of blood remained. At the side of the head a large wad of cotton wool and a thin linen bandage covered the gaping wound left by the gunshot. Someone had closed the man's eyes but Megarry still recognised the face, wounded and brutalised as it was. He noticed the unshaven chin, the thick hairs peeping from the nostrils, the ugly scar on his right cheek.

Ryder bent over and placed his chubby hand on the forehead, turning it sideways to reveal a thin black hole at the base of the ear. 'There's where he got it. Bag over the head to prevent the brains splashing everywhere and then a single round. Very efficient in its own way.' He noticed that Megarry hadn't replied. 'You've seen enough? You're happy?'

The police chief nodded. Ryder reached down and pulled the sheet back up to cover the face.

'Know what it was all about?'

'No,' Megarry said. 'I've no idea.'

Ryder started to push the trolley back into the wall. 'I took some photographs. They're being developed. You can have copies if you want. They might come in handy.'

'Thanks,' Megarry said. 'There's one other thing.' He touched the doctor's arm. 'I don't want anybody to see him for forty-eight hours. Just to give me a breather. Not even relatives.'

'What do I say?'

'Just say you're still carrying out tests. I'll take responsibility.'

'Sure,' Ryder said. He was smiling again. 'He's not going anywhere.'

The cabinet slammed shut with a bang, causing a little plastic identity tag to dance on its string. Megarry lifted it and studied the name scrawled with a felt marker. John Joseph McCarthy, it said. He let the tag fall free.

'Can I offer you a drink?' Ryder said. He sounded like he wanted to talk.

Megarry shook his head. 'I'd better get back.'

# 4

Blair turned from the cooker and waved the teapot. It was a cheap aluminium job, the bottom burned black from constant use. 'How do you like it?'

'Milk, no sugar,' Megarry said. 'Do you mind if I smoke?' He pulled across an ashtray without waiting for a reply.

'No,' Blair said. 'You just fire away.'

He poured out two mugs of tea and switched the gas off with a plop. The sound seemed to fill the little room, with its sparse furnishings, bare desk and three hardback chairs. He stared at the back of Megarry's head and spoke in a soft sycophant's voice, 'I've no biscuits. Are you hungry?'

'It's all right.'

'I'm always forgetting to get biscuits. It looks better. Tea on its own seems very mean.'

'It's all right,' Megarry said again.

Blair brought the mugs across to the desk and sat down opposite the police chief. 'It helps people to relax when you can offer tea and biscuits. I find it puts them at their ease. They talk better.'

'I've no doubt,' Megarry said. He studied the inspector. Forty five, forty six, young enough to be still ambitious. He had the deferential air of the practiced toady. Blair put a curled fist to his thin mouth and belched softly.

'What can I do for you?' he asked.

'Tell me about David Stewart.'

The inspector toyed with his gold wedding ring. 'There's not much to tell. Innocent poor devil really. A bit older than me. Fifty I'd say, at a push.'

'What did he do for a living?'

Blair lifted the mug and blew steam off the tea. 'Farm labourer. Got work here and there with local farmers. Lifted the dole. He's been working for a man called Jack McGuigan for the past month. Odd jobs. Milking cows, feeding animals. Nothing that required any great skill.'

'So why would anyone want to kill him?'

'Search me,' Blair said. He shrugged and spread his hands and watched the police chief.

'Where did he live?'

'Just outside the village. He had a cottage. County council.'

'Married?'

Blair's mouth spread in a thin smile and he shook his head. 'No. He was single. Lived with his mother.'

'Why did you smile?' Megarry asked.

Blair assumed a solemn face again. 'He was simple. A bit soft in the head. If you'd known him, you'd understand. I can't see any woman being interested in him.'

'Any paramilitary form?'

Blair found himself smiling again, involuntarily. 'No,' he said. 'Nothing like that. He'd have been a liability.'

'Any enemies?'

'I don't think so. Of course you never know. But he wasn't that type of guy. He did his work, minded his own business. Had the odd pint at weekends. He didn't have many friends, never mind enemies.'

'Was he ever in trouble with the law?'

Blair hesitated. Megarry blew out smoke and studied him. Neat haircut, clear skin, fit. He obviously took care of himself.

'Well not really.'

'Not really? What does that mean?'

Blair lifted the mug and watched the police chief over the rim, as if trying to make up his mind. He took a sip and put the tea down on the desk again. 'I had him in for questioning last year.'

'What for?'

'We had a complaint. Some parents in the village said he'd interfered with a kid.'

'What?'

Megarry suddenly sat forward in his chair. 'Boy or girl?'

'Girl.'

'What age?'

Blair shook his head. 'Six or seven. Seven, I think.'

'Jesus,' Megarry said. 'Why didn't you tell me sooner?'

Blair looked embarrassed. 'Nothing happened. We couldn't prove anything. Stewart denied it all. Said she was making it up. The kid got confused. Kept changing her story.'

'Kids rarely make these things up,' Megarry said.

'I know that. But proving it's another matter.'

'So what happened?'

'We had to let him go.' Blair was tugging frantically at his wedding ring. 'I couldn't risk bringing charges. It was too dodgy. It was one of those no win situations. Whatever way I turned I was going to get it wrong.'

'Do you think he was innocent?'

Blair spread his hands again and tried to look away from the police chief. 'Who knows? It was the kid versus him. In the end I didn't know who to believe.'

Megarry crushed out his cigarette in the ashtray. 'And what about the parents? How did they feel?'

'Sore. There was a lot of bitching for a while. A lot of ill-feeling around the place. But it gradually died down.'

'Anybody threaten him? Anything like that?'

'Not that I'm aware of. He never complained. There was the odd remark passed from time to time. But after a while it all blew over.'

'What was the kid's name?'

'McClenaghan. Julie McClenaghan. She used to hang around his house with a bunch of other kids. He used to give them sweets and things.'

Megarry considered for a moment. 'Would any of her relatives feel sore enough to kill him?'

Blair looked shocked. 'No way,' he said quickly. 'They're not violent people. They're Christians, regular church-goers. They'd never take the law into their own hands.' He fumbled in the pocket of his tunic for a handkerchief and wiped his face.

'What about an uncle? Somebody who would harbour a grudge?'

'No,' Blair said. 'I really don't think so. They mightn't have liked him much, but I don't think anybody would have been sufficiently worked up to harm him.'

Megarry sat back in his chair and lifted the mug. 'It happens all the time. It's the best motive you've come up with.'

'But not in this case. You really have to know these people. Believe me, it's not a runner.'

'All the same,' Megarry said, 'I think you should interview them. Just check out their movements. Do it informally.'

'Of course,' Blair said. 'I was planning to do it anyway.'

Megarry sniffed. 'What about his mother?'

'She hasn't been told yet. You asked for a blackout.'

'Talk to her this evening. See what you can find out. Did he owe any money? Upset anyone? Has he been involved in anything he shouldn't have?' He stood up from the desk. 'People don't get killed for nothing. He must have done something. See what you can find out.'

Blair was smiling again. He pulled the hem of his tunic down and straightened his tie. 'Certainly. I'll get working on it right away. Do you want me to ring you?'

'If you've anything worthwhile,' Megarry said.

At the door he hesitated. 'There's something else. Did you talk to anyone about this?'

'Just Army HQ. I rang them as a matter of form.'

'Anyone else?'

'No.'

Megarry guessed he was lying. He spoke too quickly.

'Why do you ask?'

'Somebody rang the BBC. Shortly after it happened. Gave them my direct line number. There were reporters all over the place.'

'You're kidding.'

'No, I'm not. They get in the way. Clutter things up. Ask awkward questions. They stop us doing our work.'

'Why would anyone do a thing like that?'

Megarry breathed heavily and kept his eyes fixed on the inspector's face. 'Money,' he said.

On the journey back he stopped at a wayside pub, a place he remembered from the old days when he would come out here on bowling trips with his father. He paid for a whiskey at the bar and then went out into the hall to ring Nelson.

'This guy Stewart. Turns out he was a child molester.'

He heard the detective catch his breath. 'Where did you learn that?'

'From the local inspector. I'm out here now.'

'He's no record.'

'I know, they didn't have enough to charge him. But it could be a motive. You know what people are like when kids are involved.'

'You mean the parents?'

'Or a relative. An uncle maybe. They're bound to feel sore.'

'How many kids are we talking about?'

'Just one that Blair mentioned. A Julie McClenaghan. There could be more. Listen, I'm not sure he told me everything. I got the impression he was trying to protect his ass. I also think he tipped off the BBC. That would explain the phone call.'

'Uh huh.'

'I tell you what. Why don't you check out the McClenaghan family? Do it discreetly.'

'Okay.'

Megarry lifted the whiskey and took a long sip. 'Everything okay there?'

'Harvey was looking for you. They've interviewed the car owner. He's clean.'

'I figured that. Stolen car. Anything else?'

'Nothing that won't wait. Your missus rang again. She said you didn't get back to her.'

'Shit,' Megarry said. 'I forgot.'

'She sounded peeved.'

'All right,' he said quickly. 'I'll take care of it.'

'When will you be back?'

'I'm not sure. I've got a security meeting in half an hour. They're bound to be asking questions about this. After that there's a few people I have to see. Just hold the fort, will you?'

'Sure.'

Megarry put the phone down and went back into the bar and ordered another whiskey. There was a bunch of anglers crowded round the counter, men with tweed hats and waders and fishing rods wrapped in blue cloth. They were laughing and joking about a fishing trip they had just had. He took his drink and sat at a table near the door.

His father had loved to stop here on the drive back to town. A nice creamy pint after the bowling. There was something about these country pubs that appealed to him, the calm, the propriety, the measured pace of the drinking that contrasted with the frantic guzzling that went on in the city. They were what his father would call respectable. They used to sit here with the light starting to fade in the fields, father and son, talking, with only the sound of the odd motor car passing on the road outside.

His one big regret was that he hadn't been able to repay him. Take him out for a decent meal in a fancy hotel: a big steak, a bottle of decent wine. And afterwards a glass of port and a fat cigar. By the time he had the money his father was gone.

The old ghosts were hovering. His father and McCarthy. The man he revered and the traitor whose information had shaped his career. He heard again the wheedling voice whispering down the phone. Meet me at Donovan's. Come alone. I've something for you. At one stage they had been the most important people in his life. Now they were both dead.

He closed his eyes and saw a man sitting on the stairs in a little house, a heavy revolver held in both hands, preparing to fire. Megarry started to scream a warning, but it was too late. He heard the shot, saw the blinding flash, smelt the acrid cordite burning his nostrils. Beside him a man was already starting to fall, a hole the size of a fist in the middle of his forehead.

He heard a voice asking something. He shook his head. A young girl with a tray was bending over him.

'Can I get you another drink, sir?'

Megarry looked at the empty glass and for an instant he hesitated. 'No,' he said. 'It's all right.'

The room was filling up when he arrived, middle-aged men in neat pin-striped suits and a sprinkling of well-tailored uniforms. And briefcases. Everybody seemed to be carrying a briefcase. There was a buzz of low-key conversation. It hung like a pall over the room. Megarry squeezed into a seat and immediately regretted not having had another drink.

The man beside him turned and smiled. He was thin and athletic, one of those well-preserved types who could just as easily be forty as fifty. He looked at the police chief over his half-moon glasses and inclined his head in a slight gesture of recognition. Megarry remembered meeting him before. He was a civil servant in the Ministry of Defence, ordnance or something like that.

'How are you today?' the man said.

Megarry puffed out his cheeks. 'Fine. Working too hard, I'm afraid. I could do with a break.' He grinned and returned the man's smile. It was meant as small talk, a throw-away remark, but the man seized on it.

'You should get more exercise. What do you do? Do you do anything? Cycle, swim? Anything like that?'

'Afraid not,' Megarry said. 'I haven't time.'

'Come on,' the man said. He drew back and observed the police chief in a semi-mocking way. 'Make time. Organise yourself. You're a manager. Why don't you delegate? Get other people to do the work. There must be somebody you can trust, for God's sake.'

Across the room, Megarry spotted Drysdale, the RUC chief. He saw him mouth something and start to come over, but someone detained him and began to talk.

'What about golf?' the thin civil servant said. 'Ever think of that?'

Megarry shook his head and smiled again. What did Drysdale want to tell him? It seemed as if he was trying to warn him about something. He looked across the room again, but the RUC man had his back turned to him now. A tall man in a bow tie had a finger raised and was chatting vigorously.

'You'd be surprised how much exercise you can get from a round of golf,' the civil servant was saying. 'Walking up and down the fairways. Better still if you carry your clubs.'

'I never thought of that.'

'Sure. And you'd feel better. You'd have more energy.' He pushed his glasses up his nose and examined Megarry. 'You could lose some weight. That's what has you tired.'

Megarry wished the man would shut up. He needed to concentrate. What was he going to tell them when they asked about Glencraigie? They'd want a full report and he'd no answers for them.

'Get out and about,' the man said. 'That's your problem. Bent over a desk all day. I'll bet.'

Megarry interrupted him. 'It's time,' he said. 'I don't have time. Crimes happen all around the clock. I've got to be available. And then there's the security aspect. I have to be careful where I go.'

'But that's ridiculous,' the man said. He stopped, realising he might have gone too far. 'Look. I'm in a club.' He fumbled in his wallet and produced a little white card. 'It's totally secure. You could play there early in the morning. All day long. Go round on your own if necessary, you don't even need a partner. Here,' he said. 'Take it.' Megarry slipped the card into his breast pocket. 'I can get you enrolled. I know the captain. Talk to me.'

'Thanks,' Megarry said. 'I'll consider it.'

There was a flurry of activity at the top of the table and people began to take their seats. Megarry looked up to see a small man in his early fifties enter the room, accompanied by a handful of personal assistants. He was wearing a neat double-breasted suit and horn-rimmed glasses which gave him a slightly owlish look. His hair was ruffled and in need of a trim. For all the obvious deference which people were paying, he could have been a schoolmaster about to take a class.

The secretary of state looked quickly around the room and then sat down, motioning for the others to join him. The buzz of conversation died away. He poured some water from a jug and one of his assistants passed round a sheaf of agendas. Megarry glanced quickly at the paper. There it was, item number three. The Glencraigie murders. He felt a tightening in his chest.

The secretary was on his feet. He pulled out a white handkerchief and wiped his mouth, then bent his head and began to give them a report on a series of meetings he'd been having with political leaders. He was reporting progress. Slow but steady. No one thought it was going to be easy.

Megarry watched him closely. He had an odd habit of addressing the wall at the far end of the room, avoiding the faces turned anxiously now towards him.

His speech was coming to an end. He had the handkerchief squeezed into a ball, clutching it tight in his left hand while he looked past the eager faces to the back of the room. He sat down and reached for the water jug and the table burst into applause.

The Commander Land Forces slowly got up from the table. He thanked the secretary, then launched into a detailed breakdown of arms seizures and arrests. People were coming forward with information. The tide was turning. He stopped and looked at each face in turn as if his message was meant for them personally.

'Don't underestimate the courage it takes to help the security forces. It takes guts. We all know how ruthlessly the terrorists deal with people they regard as informers. A bag over the head and a bullet in the back of the neck. That's often their reward. But we need these people. We couldn't operate without them.'

There were a few murmurs of assent and the Commander moved on. Megarry thought briefly of McCarthy, lying in the battered Ford Cortina with his brains blown out. He saw again the boyish face pleading for one more chance, clutching his arm like a rejected lover, and that awful defeated look in his eyes as he sent him away. Was that what had happened to him? Had he just run out of luck in the end? One job too many?

He suddenly became aware of a silence and the faces

turned in his direction. The Commander was looking down the table, a polite smile creasing his lips.

'Superintendent,' he said. 'The Glencraigie murders. Would you bring us up to date?'

Megarry felt his heart thump. What was he going to say? He looked at the row of suits and uniforms. The thought struck him that this was just a game. Some awful schoolboy sport designed to test his endurance or catch him out. It wasn't a meeting of minds, more an inquisition. He gripped the table tightly and got to his feet.

'I'm afraid there's not much to report.' He knew immediately that it sounded wrong. 'I mean we've made some progress in our enquiries but it's too early to draw any firm conclusions.'

The secretary of state was toying with his glass. Here and there a few people shifted in their seats. Megarry pressed on.

'We've identified the murdered men. One of them was a local, David Stewart, farm labourer, law-abiding as far as we can ascertain. No paramilitary associations. The second man was John McCarthy, with an address in West Belfast. Mr McCarthy had previous terrorist involvement and a number of convictions for petty offences over the past few years. They were also from different religious backgrounds. Mr McCarthy was a Roman Catholic. Mr Stewart was Presbyterian.'

'What about motive?' he heard someone ask.

Megarry glanced up, but the faces all looked the same. 'Not yet. We're trying to establish if the men were acquainted and what they were doing at the scene.' He turned towards the Commander. 'I've received a preliminary forensic report. Gunshot wounds in both cases. However they seem to have been killed by different weapons. And at different times. At least four hours' difference according to the pathologist.'

He could hear the words echoing back at him. It sounded like a prepared script, like something he'd learnt by heart, routine, unconvincing. He suddenly felt tired of all this nonsense. It was just so much play-acting. Most of these people knew nothing about police work. They were spectators, busybodies, theorists, with their text-book strategies that they'd learnt in military college. He sensed that they despised him and it made him afraid.

'It's a difficult case,' he heard himself saying. 'I can't pretend to have an early resolution. But I will keep you up to date with any progress.'

He sat down. He could feel the blood singing in his ears. His report had sounded hopelessly inadequate. Would they let it rest at that? Across the table he saw Drysdale nodding vigorously, trying to reassure him.

The Commander ran his fingers through his hair. He placed his palms flat on the table and looked around the room. Beside him the secretary of state stared straight ahead. The Commander cleared his throat.

'Thank you, superintendent. I appreciate the problems you've encountered.' He paused. 'If there are no questions we'll move on to the next item.'

There was a polite cough. Megarry looked up quickly and felt a wave of apprehension rise in his breast. From the far end of the room a tall man in his early forties was getting to his feet. Megarry recognised him at once. He had been one of his chief tormentors in the past. The room fell quiet. The man turned his narrow face towards the Commander and tugged impatiently at a small military moustache.

'Mr Fleming? You have a question?'

'I do, sir. With due respect, I think Mr Megarry is being somewhat vague.' He nodded deferentially to the politicians across the table. The secretary of state turned and looked at him, the owl eyes scrutinising his face from behind the thick glasses.

'In what way, Mr Fleming?'

'Well, sir, I think he could be more specific about who was responsible. And motive. I don't think it's good enough to say he has no idea. We could be looking at another round of sectarian murders, for instance. Surely we can expect some guidance from the police officer in charge of the case.'

Someone said 'hear, hear' and there was a murmur of approval. Fleming was seated again, smoothing his moustache with his fingers, his watery gaze turned full on the police chief.

Megarry suddenly felt short of breath, as if the air in the room had dried up. He struggled to his feet again. 'There's no evidence to suggest that these murders were sectarian. No organisation has claimed responsibility, which is unusual in itself. Until I have more information, I intend to keep an open mind.'

As he sat down Megarry noticed that his knuckles were white where he had been gripping the table. Fleming was getting up once more. He had no intention of letting go. Around the room several members of the security committee were sitting back in their chairs now, clearly enjoying the contest. He heard Fleming begin again.

'I don't wish to labour the point, but perhaps Mr Megarry underestimates the potential seriousness of the situation. We've just heard the Commander explain how close we are to defeating the terrorists.' He turned an ingratiating glance in the direction of his boss. 'Another round of sectarian murders could destroy that, set us back for months, give the paramilitaries a breathing space. It would force us to redeploy scarce resources. It would allow them to present themselves as defenders of the Catholic community. Maybe that's what they want.'

His voice rattled on, the cultured accent grating on the police chief's nerves. He kept calling him Mr Megarry, refusing to concede his proper title of superintendent. Megarry was convinced it was deliberate, done to goad him. He felt like a trapped animal, baited, nowhere to turn, the faces watching him, enjoying his plight. Under his collar he could feel the damp perspiration gather.

Fleming paused and glanced quickly round the room. 'I'm sure we'd all agree that another round of sectarian killings would be a disastrous development. It should be stopped now, before it gathers pace. That's why I believe it is vital to get to the bottom of these murders as soon as possible. I am therefore appealing to Mr Megarry to redouble his efforts.' He sat down and began ordering his briefing papers in a neat pile in front of him. Megarry was aware of a pause, an expectant hush. They wanted him to respond, to keep the game going. They smelt blood. They wanted a kill.

He looked around the room, the mass of faces turned in his direction, light glinting off glasses, off bald heads. Was there not one friend here who would help him? He looked across at Drysdale, but the RUC man avoided his glance, distancing himself from this disaster. Megarry sensed the hostility coming at him like a wave. He began slowly to rise again.

He heard a voice, strong, confident, commanding respect. He turned and recognised the tall military figure who had shaken his hand out at Glencraigie as he stepped from the Ford Cortina. The man was asking permission to speak.

The Commander took his glasses off. 'Major Prescott?'

'I feel, sir, that Mr Fleming has made his point. Superintendent Megarry has explained the difficulties he has with this case.' His thin hand gestured towards his watch. 'But we have a busy schedule and time is moving on. I suggest we take the next item.'

Outside, Megarry immediately felt better. He could breath again. There was a crush of bodies anxious to get away, people elbowing a path politely through the crowded corridor. Prescott spotted him and made his way across.

'I'd like to apologise.'

Megarry stopped and stuck his hands into his pockets, the file of briefing papers caught under his arm. 'For what?'

'For their behaviour.'

'There's no need. I survived, thanks to you. I'm very grateful.'

'It was a disgraceful performance. I don't know what got into Fleming. And the others. I'm surprised at them. They seemed to be enjoying it.'

'It's all right.'

'We're all supposed to be on the same side. For a while in there I thought that *you* were the enemy.'

Megarry found himself smiling. 'So it's not just my imagination? You noticed, too.'

'Of course. How could you avoid it? But why do they do it?'

The police chief shrugged. 'To show off, I suppose. To score points with the Commander or the secretary. Or maybe because they're bored. A bit of sport to liven up a dull meeting. They have different reasons.' They started to walk along the corridor towards the exit. 'I think some of them do it out of contempt. Fleming, for instance. He thinks I'm a bumbler. He's convinced he could do a better job than me.'

Prescott stopped and laid a hand on his arm. 'Did he have a point, do you think?'

'How do you mean?'

'What Fleming said. Maybe it is sectarian. That could be a serious development.'

Megarry was shaking his head. 'I don't think so.'

'But it's a possibility?'

'Everything's possible.'

'But it would make sense, wouldn't it? A round of sectarian killings would suit the IRA. Take the heat off them. Fleming was right about that.'

Megarry saw a small man in a black raincoat hovering in the background. He hadn't noticed him before. He had a resigned look as if he was used to waiting.

'I'm not convinced of that. I don't see what they have to gain. And where does McCarthy fit in? He was a Catholic.'

'But Stewart was a Protestant. And they've killed Protestant civilians before.'

'If they think they're involved with the security forces, yes. Or mixed up with Loyalist paramilitaries, or informing. But as a general rule, we're the enemy: you and me; the army; the RUC; the RIR.' He stopped. 'Anyway, how do we know it was the IRA? Nobody's claimed responsibility.'

'But they're the most obvious candidates.'

'Obvious isn't always right. I can only go on evidence. At the moment I've very little.'

'So you've no idea who did it?'

Megarry pursed his lips. 'I'm making certain enquiries. We could be dealing with two different cases. Maybe even two different murderers.'

Prescott looked at him with astonishment. 'You can't be serious!' he said.

Megarry smiled again. 'I am.'

The talk was loosening him up. He found himself relaxing. Here was someone listening for a change, taking him seriously.

Prescott stuck out his hand. 'I'll have a word with the Commander. I don't think they appreciate the difficulties you have. You're doing a good job.'

'Thank you,' Megarry said.

'Keep in touch. I might be able to help you. Have you got my number?' He reached into his pocket and pulled out a notepad. 'Here,' he said. He scribbled six digits and tore the page from the book. 'That's a direct line. Feel free to call any time.'

Megarry looked at the paper quickly and folded it away.

'I hear things,' Prescott said. He signalled to the man in the black coat who got up from a seat near the wall and hurried in their direction. Prescott turned again to the police chief. 'Don't be thrown,' he said, 'by criticism. Just do what's right.'

Drysdale was waiting for him in the car park. Megarry thought he looked sheepish. He leaned against the bonnet of his car with his briefcase folded across his lap.

'I'm sorry about that,' he said. 'I just couldn't think of anything to say.'

Megarry didn't reply. Instead, he took out his cigarettes and fumbled with a match.

Drysdale continued. 'I tried to warn you. He was telling anyone who would listen that this was a significant case. Then Hamilton detained me and I couldn't get away.'

'I'm getting used to it,' Megarry said.

'He wouldn't let go, would he? Like a dog with a bone.'

'I've come to expect that. It's the others who worry me. The lack of support. The Commander, the secretary. They let him do it. If it hadn't been for Prescott I'd still be getting hammered.'

Drysdale lowered his eyes. 'Cover your ass. First rule of police work.'

'Thanks!' Megarry said. He turned to walk away.

Drysdale stopped him. 'Calm down, I'm trying to be sympathetic. I don't enjoy it any more than you do. But you have to fight back. You looked punch drunk in there.'

Megarry stared at the RUC man. He had taken his cap off and was wiping his brow. The sun seemed to sparkle on his silver hair.

'How's it going, anyway?' Drysdale said. 'Can I do anything to help?'

Megarry waved his hand. 'So. So. The guy in the car, John McCarthy, was a tout. I didn't tell them that. I used to know him. He was very good. But I haven't seen him for years. The other man, Stewart, seems to be clean. Except for one thing. Last year there was a complaint against him for child molesting.'

'What's the connection?'

'I don't know if there is one. There's something else. McCarthy was shot through the head. With a Browning pistol.'

Drysdale suddenly looked up. 'You're sure of that?'

'Positive. I got the forensic report yesterday afternoon.'

Drysdale had the car door open. His face looked grave. 'Look,' he said. 'I'd keep that information to myself if I were you. It won't do you any good. Why don't you concentrate on Stewart? You'll probably find it's the IRA. They do most of the killings.'

# 5

The moment he pushed open the door he became aware of the hub-bub. The place was crowded. At a table near the bar a fat woman was singing. She had her head thrown back and the veins on her neck looked like blue pencil marks. She stopped as Megarry let the door swing closed and stepped into the room. Beside her a sparrow-like man in a sailor's cap looked up and smiled.

'It's Charlie,' the woman said.

She pushed the cap down over the little man's head and swirled the drink in her glass so that the ice rattled.

Megarry tried to ignore her, squeezing past the crowded tables, but she reached out a hand and grabbed his coat.

'Good old Charlie,' the woman said. 'He'll buy a girl a drink.'

'Hello, Doris,' Megarry said softly.

Near the back of the room he could hear the gentle clack of billiard balls colliding and make out the dark shapes of men bent over a table. It was quiet there and safe. That's where he would go.

The woman tried to caress his leg, but he lifted her hand away. 'What are you drinking, Doris?'

'Gin. Gin makes you sin. The story of my life.' She laughed, a shrill raucous cry and ruffled the little man's hair.

Megarry detached himself and made his way up to the bar. A surly man in a striped waistcoat stood with his arms folded and watched the racing on television. He turned reluctantly to take the police chief's order.

'Large Bushmills and a bottle of stout.' Megarry took out a ten pound note. 'And give Doris a drink. Gin.'

'Ice and water for the whiskey?'

Megarry nodded. 'How's the racing?' he said.

'Poxy,' the man said over his shoulder as he poured the drinks. 'Bloody favourite fell in the first. Did you have a bet?'

Megarry shook his head. 'Just interested.'

He examined himself in the mirror behind the bar. It was one of those old-fashioned ones with elaborate gold lettering and a picture of a distillery with smoke coming out of a chimney. John Power Premier Whiskies, it said. His plump face looked back at him. He waited while the barman counted out his change, then took the drinks to a table at the back. The fat woman had started to sing again: 'My, my, my, Delilah.'

As he settled down he heard the barman roaring from the counter: 'That's it. I've warned you. One more croak and you're out on the street.'

'Blow it out your asshole,' Doris said.

Megarry smiled and poured water into the glass. He sat back and examined the bar. Nothing had changed.

The same dirt and grime, unwashed windows, grease on the floor and tables. And the overpowering smell of piss and stale beer.

Behind the counter was a row of fancy bottles with exotic names, liqueurs and fine brandies, all of them empty and kept for show. Above the till a board was festooned with banknotes from foreign countries, Hong Kong dollars, yen, Dutch guilders, German marks, brown and crumpling round the edges.

He took a mouthful of whiskey and felt it warm his throat and chest. How long was it since he'd been here? Fifteen years? He hadn't been back since the last time he'd seen McCarthy alive.

The place had been full of people then, tarts and sailors from some boat that had come in, bodies pressed tight against the bar, the air filled with smoke and laughter and clinking glasses. He had pushed the envelope with the money across the table. 'I can't use you any more,' he had said.

He remembered there'd been a juke-box playing, over there where the billiard table stood. Some rock and roll song – 'Blueberry Hill'. The refrain kept running through his head.

McCarthy took the money and slipped it into his pocket without even counting it. There'd been a hundred pounds, five new twenty-pound notes. 'C'mon,' he said. He tried to smile.

'No,' Megarry said. 'It has to end.'

'Why? I've given you good stuff.'

'But you've stopped. You've dried up.'

'I can get more.'

'Look,' Megarry said. 'I can't pay you when you're not bringing in the goods. We're not the Salvation Army. I've a budget. They want to see results.' He tried to sound hard but his heart wasn't in it.

'You got me into this,' McCarthy pleaded. 'Think of the risks I took.' He kept watching Megarry with a moody hang-dog look, the scar on his cheek throbbing. His eyes began to fill up with tears. 'You can't just drop me like this. What am I supposed to do?'

Megarry could feel himself getting angry. This was taking too long. 'I can drop you when I damn well please.' He started to tell him that he'd served his purpose, that they didn't need him any more and then the jukebox started up again. Across the heave of bodies the music blared, 'My Heart Stood Still'.

'Look,' Megarry said. 'I'll see what I can do. If you get anything give me a buzz.'

McCarthy pushed the chair back and stood up and for an awful moment Megarry thought that he was going to cry. But he seemed to pull himself together. He just turned and walked out through the crowded pub without saying another word. He had never heard from him again.

A shaft of sunlight cut across the bar as the door opened and a small figure blinked in the gloom. Megarry put his glass down and watched. The man wore a cheap cotton suit, slightly too big and a shirt open at the neck. As he made his way past the tables the police chief saw that he was limping, leaning heavily on a walking stick and dragging his leg.

He stopped for a moment to exchange some banter with a group near the bar, then proceeded to the counter. From the billiard table there was a cheer as someone scored. The little man leaned forward and whispered something into the barman's face. Megarry pressed his arm against his chest and felt the reassuring pressure of the revolver. He waited till the barman turned away and then spoke softly.

'Mickey.'

The man spun round and looked in his direction. There was a moment's hesitation and then a flicker of recognition.

'Is it you?'

'Will you join me?' Megarry said.

The man hobbled over and stood looking down at the police chief. 'So the dead arose and appeared to many.'

'Dead?'

'You might as well have been. For all we've seen of you, this last while.'

'Not dead, Mickey. Very much alive.' He moved aside to let the man sit down. 'How've you been?'

'Could be worse. But what about you? Where have you been hiding?'

'Circumstances change. I'm doing different work.'

'In the same line of business?'

'More or less.'

He pointed to the man's leg, hanging loose like a stuffed rag. 'What happened?'

The man placed his stick on the table and made a great show of rolling up his trousers. An ugly white scar cut across the flattened knee-cap. 'Look what the bastards done to me.' He pushed his face close to Megarry seeking his reaction. His cheeks were studded with pock-marks and his breath smelt of beer and stale tobacco. 'Blew the knee-cap right off. Two little fuckers no more than eighteen.'

He clicked his fingers. 'Just like that.' He sniffed at the injustice of it.

Megarry nodded in sympathy. 'You must have done something.'

'No,' the man protested. 'Nothing. A little bit of fencing. Nothing serious.'

Megarry caught the barman's eye and waved for another round. He waited till the man had set down the drinks and raised his glass. 'Good luck,' he said. 'You'll get compensation.'

'Yeah. But how long will that take?' The little man sniffed again. 'And what am I supposed to live on? These things take years. Then I've got to pay these thieving lawyers. They're like piranhas. There'll be nothing left.'

'It's slow. But you'll get it.'

'I might be dead,' the man said. He lifted his glass and toasted the police chief. 'Slainte.'

'Slainte, Mickey.'

'Anyway. What brings you back?'

'Business.'

'Looking for somebody?'

'I might be.'

'Anyone I would know?' He watched the police chief over the rim of the glass. Megarry studied the undernourished face, the pale drawn cheeks with the red suppurating marks. The eyes kept moving, one eye fixed on him, the other gazing past him down the bar.

'Maybe.'

'Who?'

The police chief hesitated. He had to be careful. If this misfired, word would get out and it could ruin everything. 'Well now, Mickey. That depends.'

The man smiled to show he understood. 'You can trust me,' he said. He drew closer in a conspiratorial way.

Megarry glanced quickly towards the counter. The barman had switched the television off and had his back to them, arranging glasses. 'I'm looking for John McCarthy.' He lowered his voice. 'There's twenty quid for you if you can help me. If not, just forget all about it.'

'Is he in trouble?' the man whispered.

Megarry thought of the cold mortuary, the rattle of wheels as Ryder pulled the trolley from the wall, the sheet covering the mutilated face. 'No,' he said. 'Nothing like that.'

'You're sure? I can't get involved in anything serious. You know how it is?' He pointed to his leg. 'Next time it could be my head.'

'I just want to talk to him,' Megarry said. 'He's not in trouble. You don't have to worry. No one will know.'

The man lowered his drink and pushed the glass into the centre of the table. 'I'd need to think. When did you see him last?'

'I don't know. A couple of years? I can't remember.'

'He's changed. You wouldn't recognise him.'

'Bad?'

'He's gone to the dogs. I see him sometimes hanging around the bookies or the pubs. Scrounging drink. That sort of thing. He's not the man he was. You'd feel sorry for him.' He spread his hands in a gesture of hopelessness. 'He's split with the wife. I don't know what happened. She threw him out, I think.'

'These things happen, Mickey.'

'He's living with another woman. Up near the university somewhere. They've got a flat. She's in the same boat. Husband gone.'

'That's a shame,' Megarry said. 'Do you have her address?'

'I might have. Do you have the money?'

The police chief reached for his wallet. 'I'm going to put this twenty-pound note under the beermat. You write out the address. When you've done that, keep the money and give me the mat.' He pushed a ballpoint pen across the table. 'And Mickey . . .' He waved a finger. 'No mistakes.'

'No mistakes,' the man said. He started to scribble something. Megarry watched.

'Florentine Avenue?'

'Lisburn Road. Past the hospital. You'll find it easily enough.' He pushed the mat and the pen back across the table and finished his drink. 'I could do with a refill.'

Megarry looked at the empty glasses. 'Why not?' he said. 'For old times' sake.'

He raised his hand for the barman. Near the door the fat woman had started to sing again, her voice harsh and out of tune: 'But come ye back, when Summer's in the meadow.'

The police chief found himself smiling.

'What's so funny?' the little man said. 'Is it Doris?'

Megarry nodded.

'It's all right for you,' the little man said. 'You only come here once in a blue moon. I've got to listen to her all the bloody time.'

He found it easily enough. A long, tree-lined avenue of decaying Victorian villas. They had once housed the city's linen barons; now they formed the heart of bedsitterland. The garden of number fifteen was overgrown and the paintwork around the windows was peeling in the afternoon sun. Megarry pressed the bell and watched through the frosted glass till a tall figure came out of a room somewhere and ambled along the hall.

'I'm looking for Mrs Clancy,' Megarry said.

The tall man stood in the doorway and cocked his head back, looking down the length of his beard. 'She's not in.'

'Any idea when she'll be back?'

'Afraid not.'

The man narrowed his eyes. 'Are you a friend of hers?'

'Sort of,' Megarry said.

'Well look, she went out about half an hour ago. Can't be far. Left the kids up there.' He pulled the hall door back. 'Do you hear them? Do you hear the racket they're making?' He appealed to the policeman. 'How am I supposed to study?'

'Maybe you should talk it over,' Megarry said.

'Talk it over? Are you joking? I'm sick of talking. You don't know Marion. She never listens.'

Megarry turned away from the door. 'I'll come back.'

'Shall I say who called?' the man shouted down the path.

'It doesn't matter,' Megarry said.

He drove to the Florentine Inn and had a bowl of soup and a sandwich and read a morning paper which someone had left behind. When he got back to number fifteen, the woman had returned.

She was a small thin blonde, about thirty-five. She came to the door quickly, as if she'd been expecting him. He put his foot into the hallway and showed his ID.

'Police, Mrs Clancy. I'd like to talk to you about John McCarthy.'

'He's not here,' she said and tried to close the door.

'This will only take a moment.'

'He's not here. I don't know where he is.'

He shoved his foot further in the door. 'You might be able to help me.'

There was a rustle down the hallway and Megarry saw the bearded student. 'Having trouble, Marion?'

'No,' she said. 'No trouble.' She sighed and faced the police chief again. 'What's he done?'

'He hasn't done anything. I just need to talk to him. That's all.'

She looked confused for a moment and then relented. 'You'd better come in.'

Megarry followed her into the hcuse and closed the door. 'It's up the stairs,' she said and walked quickly across the hall.

Someone had been cooking onions and the smell was all over the house. He noticed the tired furniture, the frayed carpet, the aspidistra that needed watering. On the wall was a picture of a wide-antlered deer drinking at a brook.

At the top of the stairs two small faces peeped from behind a bedroom door. They watched the strange man climb closer till he reached the landing and then they suddenly bolted back in and slammed the door shut. He could hear them giggling and whispering.

'They get bored,' the woman said. 'Cooped up here all day.' She ushered him into a kitchen. 'I was going to take them to the park this morning but I didn't get time.' She shrugged her shoulders in a gesture of resignation.

'What about school?' Megarry said.

'School's over. This is the worst. They've nothing to do.'

He glanced around the tiny room, piles of dirty washing in a basin beneath the sink, the breakfast remains on the draining board, bits of cornflakes sticking to the cheap plastic bowls.

'Were you here before?'

'About half an hour ago.'

'Frankie told me. He's the guy downstairs. He keeps an eye on things when I go out.' She pulled over a chair for him and moved to fill the kettle. 'Cup of tea?'

'Why not?' Megarry said. Above the sink was a plastic sticker: 'Life's A Bitch and Then You Die', in yellow and black letters.

'How long have you lived here?'

56

He heard the gush of water into the kettle. 'About two years. I'm waiting for a corporation flat. This place isn't really suitable for kids. Nowhere to play.'

'Too small?'

'Way too small. They need a garden. Other kids. I'll have to move.'

'Tell me about John.'

There was a pause and a soft plop as the gas ignited. 'What's he done?' the woman said again. She came and stood before him, a cup and a tea-cloth in her hand.

'What's he usually do?'

'Nothing serious. Small time stuff. But he's been clean for a long time now.' She lowered her eyes. 'Is he in some kind of trouble?'

Megarry hesitated. It was what they always said when a cop came round asking questions. He'd never found an easy answer. 'You tell me,' he said. 'Nobody seems to know where he is. I thought maybe you could help. I heard he'd been staying here.'

'Staying here? He's living with me for Christ's sake. Didn't they tell you that?' Suddenly she seemed to get angry. 'Who sent you here anyway? Was it that cow of a wife?'

'No,' Megarry said. 'I haven't been talking to his wife.'

'She's just a slut. You wouldn't want to believe anything she would say.'

Her aggression surprised him. He put a hand on her arm. 'Calm down, Mrs Clancy. I just want to ask a few questions. I won't be long.'

'What kind of questions?'

'What he's been doing? Where he is? When you saw him last?'

'Look,' the woman said. 'Maybe you tell me what this is all about.'

'It's just enquiries. Nothing to get excited about.'

'Who's getting excited?' She was screaming now.

Megarry took a deep breath. 'I could do this the hard way. Get a warrant. Who'd look after the kids?'

She twisted the tea-cloth in her hand and he saw the cockiness ebb from her. She's just a poor beaten woman, he thought. Everyone who comes to her door brings trouble.

'Sit down. We'll talk.'

He pulled out his cigarettes and slid one across the table. She bent her pale face into the guttering match and he noticed the thin lines creasing her forehead, the dark pools forming beneath her eyes. She's been pretty once, he thought. But life has been hard. She took a deep pull on the cigarette.

'Let's start at the beginning. What's he been up to recently?'

'Not much,' the woman said. 'Drawing the dole. Getting bits of work here and there. He's no trade. It's not easy.'

'What do you live on?'

'His unemployment benefit. I get separated wife's allowance. My husband's supposed to give me maintenance for the kids, but the bastard never pays a cent.'

'How do you get by?'

She blew out smoke. 'We manage.'

'Has he been drinking?'

'A bit. Now and again. But he's never violent. He just comes home and sleeps it off.'

'And where is he now?'

'I told you. I don't know. I haven't seen him for days.'

'How many?'

She counted on her fingers. 'Five. He's been gone five days.'

'Five days?'

'That's right. Last Friday. He got a phone call around breakfast time. Just said he had to go off for a bit. So he packed a bag and left.'

'Without saying where he was going?'

'I didn't ask. I assumed it was a job somewhere.'

'And have you heard from him since?'

'I got a note. Yesterday. He sent me a few quid.'

'Would you still have it?'

'I might.' She pulled a handbag from the back of a chair and began to rummage inside. 'Here,' she said. She fished out a buff envelope and handed it over.

Megarry took out a letter. There was no address, just a scribble detailing little banalities and a scrawled signature at the end. He folded it back inside the envelope and slipped it into his pocket.

'You don't think it's odd that he should go off like that without telling you anything?'

She shook her head. 'He'll come back. He always does.'

There was a whistle as the kettle started to boil. She got up and began to fuss around the cooker. 'Do you take sugar?'

Megarry waved his hand. 'You said he always comes back. Has he done this before?'

The woman poured two cups and sat down again. 'A few times.'

'Like how many?'

'Maybe half a dozen.'

'What sort of period are we talking about?'

'Well, he's been living here about eighteen months. I'd say he's done this five or six times. It's no big deal. I suppose it's work. He always comes back with money.'

'Is it always the same?'

'More or less.'

'You said he got a phone call. Do you know who it was?'

She shook her head. 'Just a call. Frankie took it downstairs and shouted up for John. I wasn't involved.'

'Does he always get a phone call before he takes off?'

'I don't know. I'm not always here.'

'Have there been any calls for him when he's been out? Calls that you might have taken? Think hard now.'

Megarry watched her, willing her to remember. She slowly put the teacup down and stubbed out her cigarette.

'There was one call, all right. About eight or nine months ago. I was up here getting the dinner ready and I heard the phone ringing in the hall. I just ignored it because normally Frankie answers it. But he must have been out. After a while I decided to go down. It was for John.'

'What did the caller say?'

'He just asked for him. I said he wasn't here but I was a friend and could I help. He said no, when would John be back, and I said I didn't know.'

'Did he give any name?'

'Yeah. Spanish name, I think it was. Spanish or Italian. Rossi. Bobby Rossi. He said to tell him that Bobby Rossi called.'

'Did he leave a number?'

'No. Just said that John would know where to find him. I told John when he got in and he went rushing down to the phone and after a while he came back up and said he'd be going away for a few days.'

'What did he sound like? Local accent, foreign accent?'

'No, that's the funny thing. He had a British accent. Sort of posh. He didn't sound foreign at all. You'd expect with a name like that he'd sound strange, now, wouldn't you?'

Megarry finished his tea. 'Anything else you can tell me?'

'I don't think so. John'll be back in a day or two. You can talk to him yourself.'

He glanced for a moment round the little kitchen with the cheap paper peeling from the walls, and the dried milk crusted around the gas jets on the cooker. He thought of his own situation, the unmade bed, dirty washing piling in the bathroom, the stale smell when he forgot to close the fridge door.

He softened his voice. 'Did he take much with him? Can you remember what he had in his bag?'

'Not much. Only a change of underclothes. A couple of vests and shirts.'

'So he wasn't planning to stay long. What's the longest he's ever been away?'

'A week. Ten days.'

'There's one other thing. Do you know a man called Stewart? David Stewart?'

She shook her head. 'Never heard of him.'

'John never mentioned him? Name never came up?'

She wrinkled her face in a puzzled look. 'Who is he?'

'Just a man.' He stood up from the table. 'I'll hold on to the letter for a while if it's okay.' He rummaged in his pocket and produced a card. 'Here. That's my number. If you think of anything else give me a ring.'

He became aware of a noise from the bedroom. Banging and thumping as if the kids were up to something. The awfulness of her situation seized him. He smiled, trying to reassure her. 'Thanks for talking to me.'

He started for the door but she pulled him gently by the sleeve. Something in his manner had warned her. He turned to find her eyes scared and pleading with him.

'Tell me the truth. Is he all right?'

Megarry hesitated. 'He's dead. We found him yesterday morning out near Glencraigie. He'd been shot through the head.'

Her face fell apart.

He moved quickly for the door, swinging it closed behind him. As he started down the stairs he heard a roar of laughter. It seemed so out of place till he realised it was just the kids again, up to something in the bedroom.

It was getting dark as he pulled the car into the quiet street. The light was fading and black thunder clouds rolled in over the rooftops, threatening rain. The air suddenly felt cold and damp, charged with electricity. He drove a few yards past the gate, then knocked the engine off and waited.

The street was silent, the houses grey blocks in the dying light. Against a fence a kid's bicycle stood abandoned, its owner gone indoors. On a lawn he saw the pale shadow of a tent, children's toys scattered on the grass. He undid his seatbelt and stepped out onto the road.

The house was in darkness. It stood at the end of a leafy drive, the chimneys just visible against the dull skyline. He walked to the gate and then hesitated, seized with indecision. His head felt light from too much whiskey, his stomach empty. He realised he should have eaten earlier; now it was too late.

The thought occurred to him that she might have gone to bed. He tried to recall her routine, the little landmarks in her evening: dinner, television or a book, a nightcap before turning in. Bridge some nights, the occasional game of poker, but usually on a Friday.

He was about to turn away when he saw a light burning somewhere in the depths of the house. He opened the gate and heard his shoes crunch on the gravel of the drive.

On the doorstep the first raindrops fell, cooling his face and staining the dark fabric of his suit. He pressed the bell and listened as the sound echoed along the hallway. Something brushed against his leg. He looked down and saw a sleek black tomcat arch its neck along his trousers.

'Old puss,' he said. 'You missed me.' He bent to stroke its back and watched it stretch in welcome, rubbing its whole body against him now. He stood up quickly when he heard the sound of footsteps approach inside the house.

'Who's there?' It was a woman's voice.

Megarry cleared his throat. 'It's me.'

'Cecil?'

'Yes. Cecil.'

He suddenly felt stupid. He shouldn't have come. He should have gone back to the flat and got a good night's sleep.

'Wait a minute.'

He heard the sound of bolts being withdrawn and then the door swung open. A middle-aged woman in a pink dressing gown stood framed in the doorway. She had her dark hair done up in rollers, fluffy slippers on her bare feet.

'Jesus,' she said. 'You pick your moments.'

'I was in the area. You were looking for me.'

'That was yesterday.'

'I was busy.'

'Too busy to return a simple telephone call?'

He realised how tired he was. 'I can go if it's not convenient.'

'Don't be daft. Come in. It's all right.' She stood back from the door. 'Come on. I'm not going to bite you.'

She turned and walked away from him down the hallway. He closed the door and followed her to a small sitting room where a black and white movie was flickering on a television set.

'Sit down,' she said. 'Your coat's wet. Is it raining?'

'Just starting.'

'We needed rain. The ground's too hard.'

'I'm sorry about the call. Nelson said it wasn't urgent. I meant to ring you back and then it went clean out of my head.'

She ignored his apology and bent to knock the television off. 'Drink?'

'Okay.'

'The usual? Bushmills?'

He nodded and watched her fuss at the drinks cabinet.

'I was just about to go to bed. Another ten minutes and you'd have missed me. Once I'm in bed I never get up to answer that door.'

'That's wise,' Megarry said.

She brought the drinks and puffed up the cushions on the sofa before sitting down beside him. 'What has you so busy?'

'A murder case. Two men got killed out by Glencraigie.'

'I heard it on the radio,' she said. 'Terrorists?'

'I don't know.'

'So why do you have to get involved? Can't you just leave it to Harvey and the others?' She raised her glass in a salute and took a sip.

'I knew one of them.'

'Oh! Was he a cop?'

'No, an informer. Man called John McCarthy. He used to help me a lot in the old days.' He searched his pockets for his cigarettes. 'He's left a mess behind. Girlfriend and a couple of kids. He wasn't living at home.' He glanced briefly at his wife.

'You should slow down,' she said.

'Please.'

'Let Harvey handle it. Or Nelson. He's competent. You're always praising him.'

'It's not that simple. I've the security committee on my back.' He blew out a match and tossed it into a tray.

'Ignore them.'

'I can't ignore them. These people run the show. We're talking about the Secretary of State and the Commander Land Forces and the Chief Constable. How can I ignore them?' He sipped at his drink. 'Anyway, I feel I owe him something. Poor devil helped me a lot when I was starting out. And I got him involved.'

'Please, Cecil, spare me the dramatics.'

'It's true,' he said. He felt a surge of anger. 'We can't just turn our backs on people. Wash our hands of them. If it wasn't for me, he might still be alive.'

'For God's sake.' She got up and knocked on a small electric fire. 'Why don't you just pack it in? You look a sight. When's the last time you took a good look at yourself?'

'Don't,' he said. 'Please don't start.'

'But what thanks do you get?'

'I'm not in it for thanks. And why should I pack it in? I've done nothing wrong.'

'But look what it's doing to you.' Her voice was starting to rise. 'You're killing yourself. You don't owe them anything. Get out now while you're still ahead.'

'But that's just the point, goddammit. Some of them would love that. Why should I make it easy for them?'

He realised that they were fighting. He put his arm around her shoulder and pulled her close. 'Please, Kathleen. I didn't come here for this.'

She raised her face and he saw that she was weeping.

'Please,' he said.

She shook his arm free. 'It's no bloody use. You'll never change. We could still have a life together you and me. But you won't stop, will you? Solving the world's problems. What about your own, eh? What about the problems here on your own doorstep?' He stared at her. 'Look at what it's doing, for God's sake. You don't know what it's like for me sitting alone day after day in this bloody house, listening to the clock ticking on the mantelpiece. Get out, Cecil, please. Before it's too late.'

'I can't,' he said.

'You mean you won't. You want to fight the war to the bitter end. Your father's dead, Cecil. When are you going to accept that? This damned vendetta won't bring him back.'

He closed his eyes and listened as the words tumbled out, accusations, insults, abuse. It was always the same. What did she know about his father? She never saw him in his cheap suit and his bicycle clips, sitting long into the night at the parlour table with his greasy collection books doing his accounts. Worrying if the money wasn't right or if some poor bugger couldn't pay, because he'd have to face the wrath of the supervisor the next day. They'd killed him before he ever met her.

'It's got nothing to do with my father,' he said.

'It's got everything to do with him. Everything you've ever done since you joined the Branch has been for your father. Every single act, every single day. Every bloody arrest, you see it as vengeance. It's consumed your life. It's ruining your marriage. It's going to kill you.'

'Stop,' he said.

She shook her head. 'Look at you. You're in bits. You're

drinking too much. You're not eating. It can't last. You're going to kill yourself.'

He stood up. 'I shouldn't have come.'

'Why not? It's your home for God's sake. I didn't put you out. You can come back any time you want.'

'It always ends in a fight.'

'But it's because I care about you.'

At the door he turned as if remembering something. 'Why did you ring me? Is there some problem?'

'It doesn't matter. I wanted to talk to you.'

'How's Jennifer?'

She opened her mouth to reply and then stopped.

'You should never have married me, Kathleen.'

'It's a bit late now. Why didn't you tell me years ago?'

'I was in love with you.'

'Jesus,' she said. 'That's a laugh. You've only had one love in your life, Cecil.'

# 6

'Rossi,' Megarry said. He spelt out the letters slowly. 'R-
O-S-S-I. Maybe Rossa or Rossey or maybe just plain Ross.
Try Bobby, Robert, Bob, Rob. Any combination.' Across
the desk, Nelson was watching him. 'Get me anything you
can. If we've a file on him, get me prints, record, mugshot,
address. And give this priority. Understand? I want this stuff
fast.'

'Is he foreign?' the voice said.

Megarry raised his eyes to heaven. 'How would I know?
That's all I have. Just the name. He speaks with an English
accent, but that could mean anything. See what you can
do. And remember. Priority. *Priority*.'

'Gotcha,' the voice said.

Megarry put the phone down and turned wearily to the
detective. 'Where do they get these guys? Jesus Christ. The
simplest job and I have to spell it out. This place is falling
apart.'

'Calm down,' Nelson said.

The police chief narrowed his eyes. 'Calm down?'

'Yes. Relax. They'll get it for you. Just give them time.'

'Time? This isn't the Book of Kells we're working on. I've got a bastard called Fleming breathing down my neck and a case that's going nowhere. No clues, no motive, no arrests.'

'Fleming?'

'He's a security committee know-all. Head stuffed full of shit he learned in some military college. And he's determined to give me a hard time.' He reached for the phone again.

Nelson studied him. He looked like he'd had a decent night's sleep for a change. Clean shirt, neat shave. He'd even got his hair trimmed somewhere along the way. And the hand was steady.

Megarry was speaking again, the voice subdued this time. 'Is that the Capri? Is Alfredo there?' He drummed his fingers impatiently on the desk. 'Alfredo? It's Mr Megarry. You might be able to help me.'

'Yes, sir. How're you keeping?' a voice said.

'I'm fine, Alfredo. I'm looking for a man called Rossi. Bobby Rossi. You ever hear that name?'

'Who is he?'

'I don't know. Is he one of your people?'

'Never heard of him.'

'Name doesn't mean anything to you?'

There was a silence. 'There used to be a family here one time. But they're gone now. A long time ago. What's he done?'

'He hasn't done anything.'

'Never heard of him.'

'All right, Alfredo. You come up with anything, you let me know. Okay?'

'Sure. I'll give you a ring.'

He put the phone back on its cradle and looked across at Nelson.

'Who's this Bobby Rossi?' the detective said.

'Just a name I picked up. It might mean nothing.' He took out his cigarettes and slowly tapped one on the packet. 'How did you get on yesterday?'

'So, so.' Nelson sat upright in his chair. 'I checked out the McClenaghans. They're adamant that the kid was telling the truth. She says Stewart molested her half a dozen times at least. Used to take her into the cottage when the old woman was in bed. Gave her sweets and made her promise not to tell anyone. The usual routine.'

'Serious stuff?'

'Fondling mainly.'

'That's serious,' Megarry said. 'Who did you talk to?'

'The local clergyman.'

'And they're sore?'

'Sore as hell. Particularly the husband. He can't understand why Blair didn't press charges.'

'Sore enough to kill?'

Nelson was shaking his head. 'The minister says they've forgiven him. They only wanted him prosecuted to safeguard other kids.'

'Did you talk to anyone else?'

'I tried the doctor who examined her but he wasn't available.' He got up from the desk and walked to the window. Last night's rain had given the yard a clean well-swept look. On a rooftop opposite, a couple of pigeons were preening themselves, shaking their wings in a flurry of blue feathers. Cavehill shimmered in the sun. He turned back to the police chief. 'There's something else.'

'Yes?'

'McClenaghan says he complained to Blair six weeks before he took any action.'

'Did you mention this to Blair?'

'No. I haven't spoken to him. I thought I'd tell you first. The clergyman confirmed what Blair said about Stewart. He was a bit of a loner. Few friends. Definitely odd.'

'Any enemies?'

'Unless you count the McClenaghans, no.'

'Okay,' the police chief said. 'Did you go out there?'

'I used the phone.'

Megarry stubbed out the cigarette. 'Maybe we should pay them a visit.'

Glencraigie village was dominated by a towering chimney stack. It dwarfed the spires of the three churches, the rooftops, the sycamores on the green, the granite war memorial.

The McClenaghan's house nestled in the shadow of the chimney, at the end of a row of nineteenth-century workmen's cottages. They had been built by the mill owner; now the mill had fallen silent, but the houses remained. Some of them were dropping into disrepair, slates missing, gaps in the roof, but the McClenaghan's house was neat and tidy, the doors and windows newly painted, the front step freshly scrubbed.

Megarry grasped the knocker and gave a loud rattle, listening as the sound reverberated through the tiny house. For a moment there was silence and then a coughing sound and shuffling feet. There was a shudder and the door pulled open. A youngish woman stood in the hallway. She had red hair and a plain white blouse. In her hand she held a dusting cloth.

'Mrs McClenaghan?'

She was plainly taken aback, as if she had been expecting someone else. 'Yes.'

'We're police officers.'

'Police officers?' Her lip trembled and she had difficulty saying the words.

'We'd like to talk to you for a few minutes. About Mr Stewart.'

'Inspector Blair has been here already,' she said quickly.

'I know that. We'd like to ask you a few questions. Can we come in?'

She hesitated and then said: 'Of course. Come in here.'

She pushed open the door to a small parlour. In front of the window was an old fashioned sofa. She patted the cushions down and invited them to sit.

Megarry glanced around the room. It had an air of fallen gentility. Against the wall a piano had been squeezed; on its top rested a heap of bric-a-brac, souvenirs from seaside trips and fading photographs of bearded patriarchs. Above the door a crocheted message in pale blue colours said: 'The Lord is my Shepherd. I shall not want.'

'Is your husband at home?' Megarry said.

'Not yet. I'm expecting him any minute for his lunch. In fact, I thought when I heard the knocker . . .' She stood in the doorway, nervously twisting the dusting cloth.

'When will he be home?'

'One o'clock.'

Megarry checked his watch. It was five to one. 'Could we wait till he arrives? I'd like to talk to him as well.'

'Of course. Maybe you'd like a cup of tea?' She looked at the two men expectantly, hoping they'd accept her offer and give her the opportunity to escape.

'If it's not too much trouble,' Megarry said.

'I'll only be a minute, she said and hurried out of the

room. From the kitchen they could hear a tap running and the clatter of plates and saucers. The two men exchanged glances.

Megarry let his eye roam around the room. On a table near the piano a young girl in school uniform smiled from a picture frame. He got up and examined it. She looked about seven or eight, starched white blouse, hair unadorned, her innocent face beamed into the camera. In her hand she clasped a heavy book. Holy Bible, it said in gold lettering. He put the picture back and heard a noise behind him. Mrs McClenaghan had returned with a tray.

'Milk and sugar?' she said.

'Milk,' Megarry said. 'No sugar.' She looked at Nelson.

'For both of us.'

She poured the tea into delicate china cups and held them out for the two men.

'A slice of cake? It's walnut. I baked it myself.'

'You're very good,' Megarry said. 'We weren't expecting this.'

The woman smiled, clearly pleased.

'Is that your daughter?' Megarry pointed towards the picture beside the piano. 'Is that Julie?'

She looked up and the smile faded. 'Yes.'

'Where is she now? Is she at home?'

'She's in Portrush, with the Christian Endeavour.'

'Ah,' Megarry said and nodded his head. 'A little holiday.'

'They go every year. They've a hostel there.'

He noticed that she hadn't poured any tea for herself.

'Portrush's a grand spot. Good sea air. She'll enjoy that. I used to go myself when I was young. Have you any other children?'

'I've a wee boy. Norman. He's five.'

'Is he in Portrush, too?'

'No, he's with his granny in Ballymena. He's too young for the Christian Endeavour. They have to be seven, you see. His granny has a farm.'

'And what age is Julie?'

There was a shadow on the woman's face again. 'She's eight. She'll be nine next December.'

'So you and your husband are on your own right now?'

'Yes. He doesn't get his break till the end of July.'

'What does your husband do, Mrs McClenaghan?' It was Nelson. He spoke with his mouth full of cake, crumbs speckling his chin like grains of sand.

'He works for Mr Ferguson down at the meat plant.'

'Is he a butcher?'

'No. He drives a van.'

'Good steady work,' Nelson said. He took a sip of tea.

The woman was relaxing a little, but she still seemed nervous. The conversation was teetering towards an interrogation.

'Does Norman like the farm?'

'Ah yes. He loves animals. You know yourself, at that age.'

'Who lives with his granny? She doesn't run the farm on her own surely?'

'I've three brothers.'

'And is your father still alive?'

'No. He's dead.'

'And what about your husband. Does he have any family?'

'He has a brother and sister. They're both in Canada.'

Nelson toyed with his tea cup for a while and then took a sip.

The woman stood uneasily with her hands clasped in front of her. She had a thin face, plain but not unpretty, and a nose that was too narrow. As well as the white blouse she wore a heavy tweed skirt and good sensible shoes. The clothes were those of an older woman, someone in middle age.

'This is a sad business,' Megarry said, breaking the tension.

'It's awful,' she said.

'Why would anyone want to kill Mr Stewart?'

'I don't know. I suppose it was the terrorists.'

'Were you surprised?'

'I was shocked. Everyone was.' Her face had gone pale. She had started to rub her hands, like someone trying to erase a stain.

'Did he have any enemies?'

'Enemies?'

'People who would wish him harm?'

She opened her mouth to say something and suddenly she was interrupted by a loud rap at the front door. The three people exchanged glances.

'That will be Eric,' Mrs McClenaghan said. She looked relieved. 'Will you excuse me?'

They heard the scrape of the front door opening and a mumbled conversation in the hall. Next moment a thickset man was standing in the room.

The police chief put the teacup down and stood up. 'Superintendent Megarry.' He gestured towards the other chair. 'This is my colleague, Detective Nelson.' He held out his hand, but the man refused it. They watched him fold his arms in a defiant pose.

'We've already spoken to Inspector Blair.'

'I know that. I'd like you to talk to me. Just a few general questions.'

'I have to get my lunch.'

'Would you like to eat first? We don't mind waiting.'

The man looked quickly towards his wife. 'Maybe we'd better get it over with.'

He pulled out a chair beside the piano and sat down. Megarry noticed the thick neck, the broad forehead with the sweep of black hair that somehow reminded him of a bull's head.

'I want to say immediately,' the man began, 'that I resent this. This is the second visit we've had from the police. We've done nothing wrong. We're the people who have suffered. I don't see why you have to keep bothering us.' His wife had come to stand beside him and was squeezing his shoulder.

Megarry waited till he had finished. 'You're not under suspicion,' he began. 'We're only making enquiries. We hope to talk to lots of people.'

'I told Inspector Blair everything I know.'

'We might ask you different questions,' Nelson said.

'All your questions are the same.' He sat with his arms folded and stared at the floor.

'Did Mr Stewart have any enemies?' Megarry prompted.

'How would I know? I hardly knew the man except to say hello to in the street.'

'Why would anyone want to murder him?'

'I've no idea.'

'Would you say he was inoffensive?'

'No, I wouldn't. He molested my daughter. An innocent eight-year-old child. That's hardly inoffensive. I reported it to the police but, of course, nothing was done about it.'

'Inspector Blair says he hadn't enough evidence.'

'He didn't try very hard. The child herself could have given evidence. He didn't even question Stewart until six weeks after we made the first complaint.'

'When was that?'

'The first complaint?'

'Yes.'

He turned to his wife. 'Last September. We complained three times in all before any action was taken. In the end it was just a waste of time. Nothing was done about it.'

'What did you want done?' Megarry said.

'I wanted him put away. He was a danger to children. Any parent would have wanted the same.'

'And how did you feel about him?'

McClenaghan stuck his chin out and narrowed his eyes. 'I hated the sin he had done. But I forgave him. Our Lord Jesus Christ taught us to love the man who does harm to us and turn the other cheek. My wife and I are Christians. We have been born again. I forgave him the injustice he had done to us, as our Lord Jesus taught.' It sounded like a sermon he might preach in the local church.

'That's very commendable,' Megarry said. 'But you did make threats around the village.'

'Threats?'

The police chief slowly nodded his head. 'I did not.'

'I have witnesses.'

McClenaghan suddenly looked confused. He started to bluster. 'I don't know what you're talking about.'

'I think you do, Mr McClenaghan.'

The man puffed his cheeks out and waved his hands. 'I made no threats to harm him.'

'But you made threats. What exactly did you say?'

McClenaghan looked down at the floor again and shifted in his chair. 'I said that he should be put away. That he was a danger to children. I said he should be punished. I said the police were failing in their duty.'

'Anything else?'

'No.' He seemed to regain his confidence. 'Those weren't

threats. Those were the truth. I never said he should be harmed. I only said what any parent in my position would say.'

'But the man was guilty of nothing.'

'He molested my child.'

'That was never proved.'

'Because the police refused to take action.' His voice was rising. Beside him his wife pressed hard on his shoulder. 'The child wouldn't make it up. Why should she do that? My child isn't a liar.' His face had gone red. His huge bull's neck pulsed. Pieces of spittle, like snowflakes splattered his lips.

Megarry sat still. He began to drum his fingers on the arm of the chair. 'Tell me something,' he asked. 'Are you glad he's dead?'

There was a silence in the room. For a moment McClenaghan kept his head bowed. Then he looked up and stared at the police chief. 'Yes I am. He was an evil man. It's better that he should be out of the way. Glencraigie is a safer place.'

Megarry looked quickly at the woman. Her face had gone pale. In his chair McClenaghan sat unperturbed, the great bull neck bent forward, unrepentant.

The police chief stood up. 'Thank you for the tea.' He smiled at the woman but she continued to grip her husband's shoulder. 'And for the cake. It was very good of you.'

Megarry stopped before McClenaghan and stretched out his hand again. The man hesitated and then slowly reached out and grasped it.

'What did you make of that?' Nelson said as they walked back to their car. The town had come alive, lunchtime had released people from their workplaces and they were free to do some shopping. As they passed the bank they could see a queue of customers waiting for the solitary teller.

Megarry sniffed. 'I'm not sure about all that business of hating the sin, but not the sinner. It doesn't usually work like that.'

'And there's the three uncles.'

'Yes,' Megarry said. 'There's the three uncles. Why don't you check them out?'

Nelson bent to open the car door. 'Who were the witnesses you had?'

'Witnesses?'

'You said you had witnesses that he was going around making threats.'

Megarry smiled and settled into the passenger seat. 'That was just something came into my head.'

Stewart's cottage was a single-storey affair, built with limestone, near where the railway used to run. It was the last in a row of about a dozen, well maintained by the local council. In the garden, wild roses and lupins were in bloom.

The door was ajar. Just inside in the kitchen they could see an old lady dozing in a chair. Megarry gave a polite knock and waited till another woman, a thin angular type with a fussy professional air, came bustling out to ask what they wanted.

'We're police officers,' Megarry said. He had his plastic ID card at the ready. The woman studied it and handed it back.

'We'd like to have a few words with Mrs Stewart.'

'I'm Nurse Bradley,' the woman said. She puffed out her skinny chest and tried to look important. 'She's very upset. It's understandable. This is a terrible thing.'

'Where is the body?' Nelson asked.

The woman stared as if he had just said something unmentionable. She cleared her throat. 'Poor Mr Stewart is at Waverley Funeral Home.'

'Has she seen him?'

'Good Lord, no. Dr Stokes wouldn't allow it. The shock would be too much. She's a bad heart. She's eighty-one.'

'Is her mind clear?' Megarry asked.

'She's on medication. But she can understand you.'

'We'd like a few words. We won't stay long.'

'Well, just a few minutes.' The woman relented. 'And don't upset her.'

The old lady was sitting in a comfortable chair propped up with pillows. She wore a thick knitted cardigan and a blue scarf. An electric fire burned in the grate. The room was stifling. The police chief sat down beside her.

'Mrs Stewart,' he began.

She turned her grey face towards him. There were thin hairs sprouting from her chin and brown snuff stains on her upper lip.

'I'm a policeman. I'd like to talk to you about Davy.'

The old eyes didn't move. A thin film like a plastic coating covered the retina.

'What was he doing the morning he was killed?'

She sat silent for a moment. Megarry thought she hadn't understood. He started to repeat the question and then the lips slowly parted. 'Going to work.'

'Who was he working for?'

'Mr McGuigan. He helped him on the farm. He had to milk the cows.'

'How long had he been working there?'

'Four weeks,' the old woman said. She spoke in a whisper.

'And what time did he leave the house?'

'Four o'clock.'

'Did he leave that time every morning?' The old head nodded. 'Where is Mr McGuigan's farm?'

'Out the Ballymena Road.'

'Is it far?'

'About a mile.'

In the background Megarry felt the thin presence of Nurse Bradley.

'How did he get to work? Did he drive? Did he get a lift?'

'He walked.'

Across the room from him Nelson stood with his arms folded. The police chief moved closer.

'Who could have done this, Mrs Stewart?'

She stirred in her chair and pulled a paper tissue from the sleeve of her cardigan. It was streaked with black marks and rolled into a ball.

'Who could have killed him?'

'I don't know.'

'Did he have any enemies?'

'No. Davy had no enemies.'

'Did anybody threaten him?'

The old face looked blank. He saw the eyes glisten over and the tears waiting to fall. Nurse Bradley started to move forward.

'It's important, Mrs Stewart.'

Her lips parted but no sound came out. Megarry bent closer. 'Did anybody threaten him?'

'There was some talk the time that wee girl made the complaints about him.'

'Yes.'

'People were very angry. But then it all died down.'

'Did somebody threaten him then?'

'There was a lot of loose talk around the village. I was afraid.'

'Who threatened him?'

The old woman sniffed. 'Blackguards.'

'Here in Glencraigie?'

'Yes.'

'Who made the threats? Do you know their names?'

She raised the tissue to her eyes and her chest started to heave.

'What were their names, Mrs Stewart?'

Nurse Bradley moved quickly and laid a restraining hand on his shoulder. 'I really think that's enough. She's getting upset.'

Megarry ignored her.

'I don't know,' the old woman said.

'You can't remember or you don't know?'

'I don't know. He wouldn't tell me.'

'This other man who was killed. Mr McCarthy. Did he ever mention him?'

She shook her head. Nurse Bradley was standing beside him now, her face creased with concern. 'Really, Mr Megarry. I think that's enough. She mustn't be upset.'

'Tell me one more thing,' Megarry said. He bent close to the old lady's chair. 'Did he ever mention a man called Bobby Rossi?'

She stared up at him.

'Bobby Rossi. Does that name mean anything? Did he ever mention that name?'

She looked from the police chief towards the nurse, as if suddenly she had lost all concentration.

'Bobby Rossi?' Megarry said again. His voice was rising.

The nurse began fussing over Mrs Stewart, puffing up the pillows, pulling the cardigan closer across her chest.

'I'll get you a tablet,' she said. She glared at Megarry and reached for a bottle on the kitchen table.

The old woman's eyes had closed and she was beginning to doze off. There was a grating noise from her throat as she breathed, like the sound of a corncrake. Her chest heaved in steady rhythm.

Megarry stood up. The room was like an oven. He suddenly realised that he was sweating, layers of perspiration soaking his collar and face. 'I suppose it's all right to look around?'

Nurse Bradley ignored him. She'd got a spoon and was mixing something in a glass. He raised his eyes to Nelson and pointed to a door beside the fireplace. Nelson moved quickly and pushed it open.

It was a bright room with the sun flooding in from a little window looking out on the garden. In the middle was a big double bed, clean white eiderdown and sheets. In a vase near the window a bouquet of wild flowers gave a scent of woodlands. On the bed a heavy nightdress lay spread out beside a table with more bottles and medicines.

Nelson closed the door. Another one stood beside it. He opened it and looked inside.

A heavy odour of must and decay met him. There was a single bed, the clothes in disarray. On a wardrobe, Nelson could see a shabby man's suit hanging from a wire coat-hanger. He pushed the door further and walked into the room and Megarry followed.

The room contained the wardrobe and bed, a table and a chair. Nelson opened the wardrobe door and the smell of mould grew stronger. Inside were a couple of jackets and trousers. A shirt gave off the smell of stale sweat. A pair of heavy workman's boots stood beside a pair of shoes, both recently polished. On the table beside the bed was a jumble of objects: books, a comb, a cigarette lighter, a black leather wallet with silver key-ring, a jar that looked like it had contained talcum powder.

Megarry opened the wallet and looked inside. There were a few notes, a couple of lottery tickets, a faded newspaper clipping announcing the death of a neighbour. He closed the wallet and put it back. He lifted the books and stooped to read the titles. They were mostly westerns with garish pictures of horses and cowboys. One was a thriller. *Mystery of Mock House* the title read, above a drawing of a man with a gun. Another had a picture of a massive heifer, head lowered, black coat shining. *Growth Promoters in Cattle*, it said.

Behind him he heard Nelson give a low whistle. 'What about this?' He had something in his hand. It looked like a card of some kind inside a plastic folder. 'I found it there.' He pointed to a drawer.

Megarry took the card and examined it. It was a bank account. He flicked it open and all at once sucked in his breath. 'Good Lord.'

He handed the book back to Nelson, his finger under-lining an entry. Nelson stared. Megarry's chubby finger rested at a typed figure. Thirty-two thousand pounds it said. He quickly turned the pages. There were entries for sums of five hundred and one thousand pounds. They seemed to go back for months. He flicked back to the fly-leaf. The account had been opened in July 1989, Royal Avenue, Belfast, an embossed stamp mark said.

They heard a noise in the other room. Nurse Bradley was moving around. Megarry raised a finger to his lips and slipped the bank account into his pocket. He opened the door and stepped back into the kitchen.

The old woman was asleep, her head tilted to one side

on the white pillows. The nurse was clearing the table. She looked up and smiled at the detectives, amicable again now that Mrs Stewart was asleep and beyond their reach.

'I hope your little chat was some use,' she said. 'This is an awful business. I'm not sure she fully realises what has happened.'

'Did you know Mr Stewart?' Megarry asked.

She shook her head. 'Not really.'

'You knew him to see.'

'Yes. But he was a little bit odd, you know. You couldn't really have a serious conversation.'

'Do you know why anyone would want to kill him?'

She stared at the policeman with obvious horror. 'No,' she said. 'Certainly not.'

Blair was waiting for them. He was in a jovial mood. He clapped Megarry on the back and led him through the station, rubbing his hands in an oily way as he went. 'I've got biscuits,' he chirped. 'I got them specially.' He moved to put the teapot on the ring.

Megarry prevented him. 'It's all right. Honest. I've drunk enough tea. Anyway, we won't be staying.' He pulled a chair out and sat down. Across the table, Nelson joined him. Blair sat in the middle. The police chief found his cigarettes.

'Well?' Blair said. He watched as Megarry blew out the wasted match and crushed it in the ashtray.

'There's a lot of things that don't add up,' the police chief said. 'A lot of loose ends. Maybe you can help.'

'Like what?'

'McClenaghan says you waited six weeks to bring Stewart in for questioning. He says he had to complain three times. Is that correct?'

Blair immediately straightened up. 'Well, now. Let's not run away with ourselves. I think I told you yesterday. It was his word against the kid's. It wasn't that simple.'

'But you could have acted on the first complaint. That's normal, isn't it?'

'It depends on the case. This is a small village. Everybody knows everybody else. If I'd brought him in straight away word would have been out in no time.'

'So you did nothing. Why did they have to complain three times?'

'Now, wait a minute,' Blair said. 'Who says I did nothing?'

'McClenaghan does.'

'What does he know? He's a religious nut. He's paranoid about Stewart.'

'So what did you do?'

'I talked to the kid. I got her story. I talked to Stewart, privately, at his house. After dark, when nobody would know. I think I behaved correctly.' He tugged at the shoulders of his tunic and looked offended.

'But wouldn't it have been better to have brought him in when these people complained? Interview him formally. It was a serious complaint. The McClenaghan's were looking for action. You had to do it in the end.' Megarry stared at him. Across the table, Nelson watched but said nothing.

'And what about poor Stewart? He'd have been branded as a child molester. Just because some kid gets a notion in her head. That's not fair is it?'

'The McClenaghan's don't think it was a notion. They're convinced he did it.'

Blair sat back, an exasperated look on his face. 'I just told you. McClenaghan's paranoid. The wife's all right. But he's a nut. He has those kids in church half a dozen times on Sundays. The wife's not allowed to wear make-up. She dresses like she's fifty and she can't be more than thirty-five. 'The little girl isn't even allowed to put a ribbon in her hair.' He spread his hands. 'That's the kind of guy you're dealing with. He gets something between his teeth and he won't let go.'

'What about the kid?'

'She kept changing her story. Times, dates, what he was supposed to have done to her. She'd never have made a credible witness, even if we'd let her give evidence, which is doubtful. And he denied it. Every time I questioned him, he denied it.'

'And you don't think he did it?'

Blair puffed out his cheeks. 'Who knows? What does it matter now? He's dead.'

Megarry stubbed the cigarette out. 'Well it might matter to her. And to her family. You talked to them. Did you make any progress?'

Blair shook his head. 'No. It was just the same. Hang-dog resentment. They blame me for not locking him up.'

Did you know Mrs McClenaghan has three brothers?'

'Sure. They're farmers. Out near Ballymena.'

'What do you know about them?'

Blair tugged at his wedding ring. 'They're small farmers. About fifty acres. Sheep and cattle. Decent people . They've never been in any trouble, that I'm aware of.'

'Could any of them have killed him?'

'Not in a hundred years. They'll bitch and complain. No doubt they did. But they're not the sort of people who are going to go out and kill somebody.'

Megarry sat back in his chair and studied the inspector, who glanced nervously from one to the other, trying to anticipate where the next blow would come from. Megarry knew exactly how he felt. Like a trapped animal. He sensed a stirring of sympathy for him.

'Did you know McClenaghan was making threats around the village?' It was Nelson this time. Blair shifted in his seat to face him.

'Sure I did.'

'Did you take them seriously?'

'No. It was just hot air.'

'Did you talk to him about it?'

'I let him know I was aware of it. I didn't formally caution him or anything. He was just letting off steam.'

'The old lady says someone made threats to Stewart.'

'Did she name anybody?'

'No,' Nelson said. 'She just said it was blackguards.'

'McClenaghan probably.'

'But it could have been somebody else?'

'Maybe. It sounds like loose talk. That's why I didn't want to act officially on their first complaint. It just lends credence to this sort of thing.'

'What about the old lady?' Megarry said. 'Did you talk to her?'

'I broke the news to her,' Blair said. 'Last night. I observed your blackout.'

'How did she take it?'

'Bad. She had to be sedated. I brought a nurse with me. She's over eighty you know.'

'Eighty-one,' Nelson said.

'Eighty-one. I brought Nurse Bradley from the village.'

'We met her,' Megarry said. 'Did you get a chance to talk to her? To Mrs Stewart?'

Blair shook his head. 'Just generally. I didn't learn anything I didn't already know.'

'You told me Stewart was a labourer.'

'That's right. He did odd jobs for the local farmers. Whenever there was work. Farmers aren't exactly the best employers.'

'And he drew the dole?'

'Whenever he wasn't working.'

'Did he have any other means of income?'

'How do you mean?'

'Was he earning money anywhere else?'

'I don't think so. He didn't have a lot of money. But then he didn't need much. He lived with his mother. Simple pleasures. The occasional pint. They weren't exactly wealthy, you know.'

Megarry paused for a moment. 'Look, I'm sorry if we've appeared aggressive. This damned thing is so complicated. I appreciate you have a difficult job. Small place, like you said, and everybody knowing each other.'

Blair suddenly loosened up. 'That's all right. The McClenaghans are plausible people. I can understand that they're upset. But I have to take a broader view. This isn't Belfast. Everybody knows each other.'

Megarry stood up and prepared to go.

'Are you getting anywhere?' Blair asked. 'Making any sense of it?'

'Bits and pieces. It's slow.'

'What about the other man? McCarthy? Anything on him?'

'We're making enquiries.'

'Anything to connect them?'

'Not so far.'

'I see. Well, if anything comes up here, I'll let you know at once.'

Outside in the forecourt a shiny Datsun was parked, almost new. It gleamed in the sunlight. Megarry ran his hand along the bonnet.

'Nice car,' he said. 'Who owns it?'

Blair looked pleased. 'I do.'

Megarry whistled in admiration. 'Good for you.'

He settled into his own car and rolled down the window. 'You ever have a murder case before?' Blair shook his head. 'Most times it's someone the victim knew. It's rarely a stranger. It could be someone here in the village. Someone you see every day.'

'Uh huh.'

'Just keep it in mind,' Megarry said.

# 7

On the way into work Megarry stopped at Harvey's office. There was a smell of cabbage. It seemed to be everywhere, as if it had soaked into the books and files, into the furniture, into Harvey's clothes.

'You were looking for me?' Megarry said.

Harvey stared up from a pile of paperwork and fixed the police chief with a quizzical eye.

'Was I?'

'Nelson told me.'

'Ah, yes. Come in.' He leaned back in his chair and played with a pencil. He rolled it methodically between his fingers. 'I've got so much to do, things go out of my head.' He looked at the police chief and smiled out of the side of his mouth. 'I got a strange phone call. A request. I thought I'd better talk to you. A guy called Fleming wanted the preliminary forensic report. I said I needed your permission.'

Megarry caught his breath. 'What did he say?'

'He said he was examining the Glencraigie case and needed to see the report. Sounded like he meant business.' Harvey rolled the pencil slowly in his fingers and studied the police chief. 'Who is he anyway?'

Megarry sighed. 'He's an advisor to the Commander. He was on about it the other day at the security committee.'

'Military?'

'I'm not sure. He wears a suit. But that doesn't mean much. He could be anything.'

Harvey nodded. 'So. Do I give it to him?'

Megarry thought for a moment, and then made up his mind. 'No,' he said.

'Fine.'

'He's got no right to it. It's not his case. We could be setting a precedent.'

Harvey bent his head to the files on his desk. 'Is he giving you a hard time?'

'He's interfering,' Megarry said. 'I don't like people interfering. They usually think they know better than I do. He's got his mind made up that this is an IRA job. Sectarian murder. To stir things up.'

'It's a point of view.'

'But it's wrong.'

Harvey sniffed. 'How can you be so sure?'

'Instinct. Stewart, the guy in the road with his head blown off? Nelson found a bank account in his bedroom. It had thirty-two thousand pounds in it.' Harvey whistled. 'The other guy, McCarthy. The guy in the car. He was a tout. Did I tell you that?'

'No,' Harvey said.

'He was. Any chance some of our people might have been using him?'

Harvey looked surprised. 'I never heard of the man

till his name turned up on that forensic report.'

'Check it out for me, just in case.'

'Where are you getting this stuff?' Harvey said.

'I talked to his girlfriend. He used to disappear on little trips from time to time. Always came back with money. He was on one of these outings when he got killed. Sounds like touting to me.'

Harvey nodded and shrunk into his chair. 'This thing is getting very complicated.'

'What I can't figure out is what use he would be. He was too old. And he was a drunk.'

'I can check,' Harvey said. He suddenly leaned forward across the desk and tapped it gently with the pencil. 'Tell me something. Why are you getting so involved in this case? Why don't you let Nelson handle it?'

'Because I *am* involved. I recruited McCarthy. I got him into this racket in the first place.'

Harvey opened his mouth. There was a sudden rumble and the walls shook. The files on the desk started to slide. There was a shudder and then a grating sound.

'It's all right,' Harvey said. 'No need to panic. Just the lift.'

Megarry wiped his forehead. 'Is it like this all the time?'

'Most times,' Harvey said. He rolled his sad eyes. His pencil had fallen on the floor.

Megarry went up to his own office, put on the coffee percolator and sifted through a pile of mail on his desk. The message he was looking for wasn't there. He lifted the phone and dialled through to Records Branch.

'Any luck with that Rossi guy?'

The voice on the other end sounded bored. 'Nothing.'

'Nothing?'

'Not a whisper.'

'What about Rossa, Rossey? I mightn't have got the spelling right.'

'No,' the voice said. 'We've tried them all. Different combinations. I've even got a call out to Dublin Castle, just in case. But I'm not hopeful. What's he done anyway?'

'It doesn't matter,' Megarry said. 'I've something else.'

'Shoot.'

'How far back do you go on murder files? Greater Belfast area?'

'How far back do you want?'

'Four years?'

'There are dozens of them.'

'Just civilians. No military. No cops.'

'I'll see what I can do,' the voice said.

Megarry lit a cigarette and waited while the coffee boiled and then on impulse he took the phone again. He listened with apprehension as the number rang out. After a minute a woman's voice came on the line.

'It's me, Cecil. Look, I'm sorry about last night.'

There was a pause. 'Where are you?' she said.

'I'm at work. Look, I was tired. Maybe it wasn't such a bright idea to call on you so late.' He found himself apologising, tired, working hard. The same rigmarole he'd been through a dozen times. He knew it off by heart.

'It's all right,' she said at last. 'You don't have to go on about it.'

'I shouldn't have stormed out.'

'I said it's all right.'

He pulled on his cigarette. 'What did you want to talk to me about?'

'Have you got time to listen?'

Something in her voice alarmed him. 'Sure. There's no one here.'

'It's Jennifer. She's sick again.'

He felt his heart sink. 'Jennifer?'

'Yes, Cecil. She's in hospital. Dr Crowley's looking after her.'

'Oh, my God.'

'I called to see her on Monday and found her in bed. She hasn't been eating for weeks. She looked awful. I rang Crowley and he came immediately and took her in.'

'No,' he said. He closed his eyes and saw the emaciated girl pushing the food away, cutting the bread into wafer thin slices, spreading the butter so fine it looked like oil. He felt a panic rising in his breast. 'How bad is she?'

'Bad enough. She's lost a lot of weight.'

'Why didn't you tell me sooner?'

'That's rich, Cecil. I phoned. I left messages. You were too damned busy.'

'Can I see her?'

'I don't think so. She's not well enough for visitors.' He caught the tension in her voice.

'She'll pull through,' he said.

'Jesus, Cecil. How can you say that? You haven't seen her for months.'

'I said she'll pull through. It'll be all right. Crowley knows what he's doing.'

He heard her begin to sob. 'Please, Kathleen. She'll be all right. Don't upset yourself.

'I can't help it. I'm worried sick.'

'Do you want me to come over?'

'No,' she said quickly. 'I'll be okay.'

'I'll call you tomorrow. Try not to worry.'

There was a click and the line went dead. Immediately

he started to ring again and then stopped. He realised that his throat had gone dry and his tongue tasted like sand inside his mouth.

He made his way to the percolator and poured some coffee. A feeling of guilt overwhelmed him. It was all his fault. Jennifer was killing herself, slowly starving herself to death. She was doing it to punish him. Even if she didn't know the reason, he did. It was because he'd been an absent father. He went back to his desk and sunk his head in his hands.

He saw her as a little girl, scrambling onto his knee for a bedtime story. Or rushing from school straight into his arms as he waited at the gate, that red velvet bow in her hair which she always insisted on. It had been 'Daddy this', 'Daddy that', 'My Daddy's a policeman'. He'd been the centre of her universe. But somewhere along the way he had betrayed her.

The remorse gradually gave way to resentment. Why hadn't Kathleen told him sooner? Last night for instance, acting so damned coy, lecturing him about the godammed job for the umpteenth bloody time. Why hadn't she just *told* him? The thought occurred to him that he should go to her, try to comfort her. She must be suffering terribly, stuck alone in that rambling house, worried sick. What had she said last night? 'You don't know what it's like for me listening to the clock ticking on the mantelpiece.'

He checked his watch. He could get there in twenty-five minutes if the traffic was slack. He started for the door and as he opened it he saw two men in shopcoats struggling with a large cardboard box.

'You ordered files?'

'Yes, that's right.'

'Where will we put them?' The men waited impatiently

for directions.

'Here.' Megarry cleared a space on his desk. 'How many have you got?'

'Almost a hundred.'

'You got them all?'

'I think so. Four years, you said.' The men put the box down and made a fuss of dusting their hands. Megarry waited till they had gone and then opened the drawer and reached for the whiskey bottle.

When he looked up Nelson was framed in the doorway. He saw that he was staring at him.

'Are you all right?' the detective said. 'You look pale.' He came and stood before the police chief. Megarry shook his head.

'It's just a dizzy spell. It'll pass.'

'You don't look well. Can I get you something?'

'I'm all right. Goddammit.' He waved the younger man away, pushed the bottle back into the drawer and closed it again.

'I'm sorry,' he said after a while. 'It was just a dizzy turn.'

Nelson sat down and pointed to the box. 'What's all this about?'

Megarry took out a folder and held it up. 'I had this idea. It struck me if we went through the files we might find something similar to the Glencraigie case. It might give us a lead.' He took out a bundle of folders and began to divide them into two lots. 'We'll split them fifty-fifty. We're looking for similarities. Anything that suggests a pattern. Anything that strikes you as the same. Weapons, victims, location. Anything at all, no matter how insignificant.' He lifted a pink file and gave it to the detective. 'That's the preliminary forensic report on Glencraigie. Study it first. It's got details of the gunshot wounds, weapons, fibre analysis. When you've done that you can start on these. We'll begin with the most recent cases and work back. Anything you're not sure about, ask me.'

He suddenly stopped as if he'd remembered something. 'I'm sorry, I should have asked. You're not tied up tonight?'

Nelson shook his head.

'Okay. It's going to be a long night. We can get coffee and sandwiches later on. I want this job finished before we leave. And one final thing.' He leaned on the desk and looked hard into the other man's face. 'This isn't going to be pleasant. There are some pretty awful details in there. You're going to learn something about man's inhumanity to man in this Christian city we live in.'

He went back and took off his watch and lit another cigarette. The queasy feeling seemed to have passed. He drained the coffee mug and lifted the first folder. On the cover was typed the name of the murder victim and the date. An official stamp said: STRICTLY CONFIDENTIAL. RUC RECORDS BRANCH. DO NOT REMOVE. He turned the pages and started to read.

It was a domestic violence case, not what he was looking for. He skipped through the list of cruelties inflicted on a wife and children, beatings, humiliation. As he read through the file, events spiralled to an inevitable conclusion. One night, as the husband lay in a drunken sleep, the woman took an axe and almost severed his head from his spine. He turned to the final paragraph. He knew the verdict already: Guilty. But the judge had allowed a defence plea of diminished responsibility. She was placed on probation. He set the file aside and lifted another.

Only a handful of the cases dealt with ordinary murder. Many involved sectarian killings, innocent people gunned down at street corners, in taxis, in pubs, cases of mistaken identity. Some were bloody revenge killings, people picked out at random to even up the body count. Many dealt with the murder of informers, caught in a web between the paramilitaries they were betraying and the police and army who bribed or blackmailed them. Their bodies were found up alleyways or in ditches, hands tied behind their backs, bags over their heads, scribbled notes pinned to their clothes to warn others.

He found himself starting to get weary with the endless catalogue of brutality. Was this what happened when you became a killer? Did it just become routine? Did you ever get tired of the bloodshed the way a labourer got tired, or a bus conductor, or a policeman? Or did it become an addiction?

The thought struck him that he was wasting his time, forcing himself to read through these bloody rolls of death. What did he hope to find? Why didn't he go and see his wife, or go home to bed, or just go off and have a drink? What was keeping him here, turning page after page?

He glanced at his watch. It was almost nine o'clock. He looked across at Nelson and, as he did so, the detective saw him and looked up.

'Find anything?'

'No,' Nelson said and stretched his arms behind his neck. He'd read through about thirty folders. About twenty remained untouched. 'Not a thing.'

Megarry grunted and started into the files once more. One by one he read them and set them aside. A stillness seemed to have settled over the room, the only sound the soft turning of a page. He felt his eyelids getting heavy and his head begin to droop.

He thought again of McCarthy. He saw a man lying in a car, a bag over his head, blood soaking the seats. When he bent closer, he saw it was a young woman. She was huddled in a bed, the sheets drawn up around her thin face. There were dark circles underneath her eyes; her cheekbones jutted like some gaunt scarecrow. He reached out to touch her and she became a laughing child. She put her arms around him and whispered, 'I love you, Daddy.' He felt his heart fill with sadness. He went to kiss her and she pulled away. 'You're a bad father,' she said. 'A bad father, a bad father, a bad . . .'

The phone woke him. He sat up with a jolt. He looked at his watch. It was five to ten. 'Who is it?' he said.

He didn't recognise the voice at first. He thought she said Margaret and then he realised it was Marion.

'You talked to me yesterday. Remember. You called to my flat. About John.'

'Of course,' he said. 'Mrs Clancy.'

'I didn't think I'd get you this late. I need to talk to you.' He thought her voice sounded slurred but it could have been the line. He looked at the pile of folders. There was another hour's work. Forty-five minutes if he was fast.

'Where are you now?'

'I'm at home.'

'Any chance you could meet me somewhere? Could somebody mind the kids?'

'They're with my mother,' she said.

'Do you know the Montrose Hotel? It's near you. On the Malone Road.'

'I know it.'

'There's a snug in the back. I'll see you there in an hour.' He checked his watch again. 'Eleven o'clock. Okay?'

'All right,' the woman said.

She put the phone down. Megarry rubbed his eyes and started back into the files.

At twenty past ten he got his break. The file looked just like all the others but the moment he started to read it the similarities grabbed him: body found in the back of a car on the outskirts of the city; lonely country road; sack over the head; behind the left ear the neat entrance hole made by a Browning bullet. He quickly turned the pages. The victim was Thomas Clarke, Roman Catholic, milk roundsman, forty-two years of age, father of four children, no criminal record. There was more. He'd been missing for five days before the body was found. No one had claimed responsibility. The crime was unsolved. In his coat pocket was a copy of *Loyalist Clarion*, an extreme Protestant news-sheet. In the margin of the file someone had scribbled in pencil: Possible IRA execution. Presence of *Loyalist Clarion* could indicate Protestant paramilitaries. In other words, they didn't know.

Megarry closed the folder. He looked across at Nelson. His head was bent over the files, slowly turning pages. He got up and went across and dropped the folder on his desk. The detective glanced up. His eyes were red.

'Read that,' Megarry said. There were about ten files still remaining on his desk. 'Can you finish those for me?'

Nelson sighed.

Megarry suddenly reached out and ruffled his hair. 'You're a good scout,' he said.

He had trouble getting in. For some reason they had the side door locked. There was a lot of cars in the car park and Megarry suspected they had a late night function. He considered going round to the front door and through the lobby but it was too conspicuous. He pressed once more on the bell and eventually saw the skinny figure of the night porter pad out from behind a desk somewhere and emerge into the light.

He recognised Megarry at once. 'It's yourself,' he said through the glass. He slid a bolt and pulled the door open.

'You're closing early,' Megarry said.

'It's a dinner dance. We're trying to keep them all in the main ballroom. It's easier if we keep this door closed. Otherwise they end up all over the place.' He stood aside to let the police chief enter and Megarry thought he caught a whiff of beer from his breath.

'Is the snug still going?'

'It is, of course.' He pushed the door closed and started to turn the lock. Megarry felt in his pocket for some change and pressed it into the man's hand.

'Many down there?'

'A few courting couples. A few stragglers. It's quiet enough.'

He started down a carpeted hallway. From somewhere in the hotel he could hear a band playing, loud laughter, the clink of glasses. The sound receded as he approached the snug. The lights were dimmed making shadows on the walls and tables and the rows of bottles behind the bar.

He saw her immediately. She was sitting in one of the alcoves and a man in a dress suit was leaning across to talk to her. He got up and moved away as soon as the police chief approached. She smiled as he sat down.

'You found it.'

'No problem.'

She wore a light cotton dress and had her hair tied back with a black ribbon. He smelt the musky scent of cheap perfume. She already had a glass half-filled with what looked like gin or vodka.

'Can I get you something?'

'Why not?' She lifted her drink and drained it and set the glass down noisily on the table.

'What would you like?'

'The same,' she said. 'Vodka and lemonade.'

The ageing barman was watching from the counter. Felix or Frank? He couldn't remember his name. He raised his hand and the man came across with a tray. 'I'll have a Bushmills, ice and water. The lady will have a vodka and lemonade. Large. Both large.'

He turned to her. 'I'm sorry I couldn't get here sooner. I had a lot of work to do.'

'That's all right. I understand. You people never stop. The long arm of the law.' She giggled and Megarry realised she was tipsy.

'Are you here long?'

'About half an hour. My mother took the kids. I just felt like getting out of the flat. This thing is a terrible shock.'

The barman approached and set the drinks on the table. He waited while Megarry fumbled for a five-pound note and then poked in the pockets of his red waistcoat for change.

'It's all right.' Megarry waved him away. The man bent his grey head and lifted the tray and retreated again behind the bar. 'Anyway,' the police chief said. 'I got here.'

He poured water from a little jug and lifted his glass. The yellow whiskey clung to the sides like oil. The first mouthful burnt his tongue. 'Good luck,' he said and put the glass down.

'I can't go to the funeral,' the woman said. 'What do you think of that? The bitch has made it an all-family affair.' She stirred the ice in the glass with her finger till he heard it crack. 'That's to keep me away. She couldn't give a damn about him while he was alive.'

Megarry looked at her. She had put on make-up so that her face looked younger, the wrinkles smoothed away. A dab of lipstick made a red mark on her white teeth. He suddenly felt tired again. Am I able for this? he thought. Can I sit and listen to this woman's problems? Haven't I got enough troubles of my own?

'What did you want to see me about?' It sounded blunt, brutal almost. Immediately he regretted it. But she didn't seem to notice. She was nattering away about the funeral, about being excluded.

'Not that I care. He's dead. Nothing can bring him back. And he loved me. That's what counts. Having a fancy funeral won't fool anybody. She should have looked after him when he was alive. People know that. Who does she think she's kidding?' She lifted the glass and swallowed half of it and put it down unsteadily on the table. 'Don't you think I'm right? Haven't I got the right attitude?'

'Sure.'

'If they don't want me, I won't go. Who cares? I have my memories. That's what counts. I know who he loved. And she knows. And she knows that I know.' She giggled and reached for the glass again. 'Can you follow that?'

Megarry found himself smiling. 'Sure. It's simple.'

'Am I doing the right thing?'

'It's the only thing you can do.'

'But that's not the point.' She waved a finger. 'Is it the *right* thing?'

'Sure, it's the right thing.'

'Okay then,' she said. 'It's all just so much hypocrisy. That's what gets me.'

Megarry lifted his glass and took a long pull at the whiskey. He could feel it loosening him up. He swished it around and then, on impulse, finished it off. 'You're falling behind.' He pointed to the woman's drink. 'Another?' He already had his hand raised for the barman.

'Why not?' she said. She lifted the glass and drained it. 'You only live once.'

'How did the kids take it?' Megarry said. 'Have you told them yet?'

She suddenly looked sad. 'Not in so many words. I told them that he wouldn't be coming back. Uncle John. That's what they called him.' She turned in her seat to look into the policeman's face. She's still pretty, he thought. Still pretty despite all the hard times. Why shouldn't she let her hair down? Poor cow. What life has she had?

'Do you know that he treated those kids better than their own father? That bastard never gave a shit about them. Never called. Never saw them. Never gave me a penny for their upkeep. They loved John. He was like a real father to them.'

'That's good. Kids need a father. Particularly boys.'

'He was great with them. Couldn't do enough for them. Always buying them little presents. Sweets, small things like that. It's the thought that counts.' He imagined for a moment she was going to get sentimental and then suddenly she cheered up again. 'I just told them he'd gone away. They can handle that better. Death? What do kids know about death? They don't understand it. This way it makes some sense for them.'

'You did the right thing,' Megarry said. The barman came and set down the fresh drinks. He searched for his cigarettes. 'You wanted to tell me something?'

She waited till her cigarette was alight. 'It mightn't be important. Just something that struck me after you'd gone.'

'Yes?'

She lifted her glass and started stirring it again with her finger. 'Somebody he was friendly with. From the old days. He used to see a lot of him. I thought he might be able to help you.'

'Who?' Megarry said.

'A man called O'Connor. George O'Connor. Do you know him?'

Megarry took out a handkerchief and rubbed his face. George O'Connor? Was he still around? He remembered George, with the squat weightlifter's frame and the boyish good looks. He was a big-shot in the old days. But he thought he'd died years ago.

'They were in the RA together when they were young. Did you know that? Did you know that John was in the RA?'

'No,' Megarry lied.

She lifted her drink and watched him over the rim of the glass. 'He was. He didn't talk about it much. But he saw a lot of George. They were pals. He was the only real pal he had. Real pal, I mean. Not these drinking cronies who only hung around him when he'd a few bob.'

'Where would I find him?'

She tossed her shoulders. 'He lives up the Falls somewhere. Divis Flats. Somewhere like that.' She suddenly sat forward. 'You know where you'd get him. At the funeral. He's bound to be at the funeral. He wouldn't miss it. If one person is at that funeral, I'll go bail it'll be George.'

Megarry put his glass down. 'Where is it?'

'St Peter's Church. Three o'clock.'

'Tomorrow?'

'Yes, tomorrow. George might be able to help you. You

never know. Maybe he can tell you where he was going when he went on these trips.'

'Maybe,' Megarry said.

She smiled coquettishly and he found himself grinning back. 'You never know. Even small things can be important. On the other hand,' she waved her arm. 'Maybe it'll be nothing.'

'I'm grateful. I'll try and talk to him.'

'Do you know why they did it?'

The question shocked him. He suddenly realised it was the first time she'd asked. It seemed like the obvious thing to know, but she hadn't raised it until now.

'No. We're no further on.'

'Maybe you'll never find out.'

'That's possible. But we'll certainly try. Very hard.'

'I can't figure it out. He was harmless. Everybody liked him. He was so generous. He wouldn't have harmed a fly. Why would they want to kill him?'

'Who knows? There's too much killing now. They've got a taste for it. Life is cheap.' He sounded like a politician, mouthing platitudes. But it was true wasn't it? Life was cheap. Just put a bag over somebody's head and pull the trigger. You didn't even have to watch them die. Like shooting a dog.

'Poor John,' she said. She reached out and took his hand and laid her head on his shoulder so that her perfume caught his nostrils again. 'He was so good.'

He felt a sudden shock, but not unpleasant. A warm tingle at the contact with soft human flesh. Around them other lovers were pressing close, whispering. The lights were dim. At the bar, Felix was reading a paper. He let her rest for a few minutes and then stubbed out his cigarette. He lifted his glass and held it up.

'One more for the road?'

She took a deep breath. 'Why not?' Her speech was slightly slurred. Not drunk, just nice. He waited till the barman had set down the new drinks.

'I'll have to go soon,' he said.

'That's all right.'

'What are you going to do?'

She sighed. 'Pick up where I left off. Life goes on.' She waved her fingers. 'There's no point grieving.'

He thought it sounded brave, profound, but he knew it was really banal. Something she had read or heard on television. She smiled her coquette's smile again and lifted the fresh drink. She reached across and clinked glasses.

'Good luck,' she said.

He nodded and drained the glass.

'Take me home.'

Megarry lifted her jacket and handbag and put the cigarettes in his pocket. In the ballroom the band had stopped playing but someone was crooning a dreary ballad. At the door to the toilet a man in a dress suit stood propped against the wall, too drunk to move. Megarry recognised him as the man who had been talking to her when he first came in.

The skinny night porter came scurrying out from behind his desk when he saw them approach. He looked surprised, but made no remark, just bent to slide the bolt from the door.

Outside the night was still warm. There were some stars in the empty sky. She laid her head again on his shoulder. 'John would understand,' she said.

# 8

Something woke him. A noise somewhere in the house, the ticking of a clock, maybe the sun seeping through the net curtains of the little window. For a moment he was unsure. He thought he was in a strange country, the landmarks unfamiliar, the bed, the furniture, the fading wallpaper. On the floor a string of clothes lay discarded, his shirt and trousers, a woman's cotton dress, the flimsy fabric of a bra, stretched like elastic on a chair.

All at once he remembered. The journey home in the car, the slow climb up the stairs, the frantic fumbling with buttons and belts in the light from the lamp-post outside the window. Then falling down here into this bed.

He realised his throat was sore, a pain was hammering in his head. A cold terror seized him and with it a stab of remorse. For some reason he found himself thinking of Jennifer and suddenly he felt guilty. He saw again her emaciated body huddled beneath the grey hospital blankets. Crowley in his white coat bending over her, coaxing her to eat. He shook his head and the body beside him stirred.

'What time is it?' She sounded still asleep. He caught a warm smell of stale drink and tobacco and fading perfume. He started to turn away.

'What time is it?' she said again. She lay against the pillow, her blonde hair matted with sleep, the make-up askew, mascara smudged like an ink-mark beneath her eyes.

He looked at his watch. 'Jesus,' he said. 'It's ten past nine. I shouldn't be here. I'll have to go.'

He started to move from the bed, but she reached out and tried to pull him down. He lay for a moment and let her wet mouth kiss his ears and neck, her hand grope between his legs. Somewhere in the house he heard a radio playing dance music. He felt a wave of nausea.

'I have to go,' he said. He pushed her away, trying to be gentle, and sat with his feet on the cold floor, willing the feeling to pass.

'Don't be like that,' she said. She sounded miffed and then all at once her voice was coaxing. 'We've all day. The kids won't be back till this afternoon. I can make you something to eat.'

'I'd love to,' Megarry lied. He stood in his bare feet and tried to fasten his trousers.

'Then stay. What's stopping you?' She reached out and playfully pulled at his shirt.

'I have to get to work.' He tried to smile. 'I've a meeting at ten o'clock. People are expecting me.' He found his socks and shoes and started to put them on.

'Oh well,' she said. She lay back on the pillows and for a moment he thought she was sulking. 'Work, work, work. Is that all you guys think of?'

'Really. I have to go. I'm late already.' His hands fumbled

with the laces. He felt a sweat break on his forehead.

'Let me get you some breakfast.' She pulled the sheets back and stepped out of bed. He saw again how well she looked, her body firm and smooth, full breasts veined in blue. He thought she would try once more to engage him, but she was bending forward, struggling with the straps of her bra. In a moment she was pulling the dress over her head.

'Coffee. Only coffee.'

She pushed her hair back and smiled. 'Not feeling well?'

'I've a sore head. It'll go away.'

'I could cook you some eggs. Toast.'

'No,' Megarry said. 'Just coffee.' He rubbed a hand across the stubble on his chin. 'I don't suppose you have a razor.'

She was pulling a brush through her tangled hair. She turned and looked at him, her head tilted sideways. 'In the bathroom. There's shaving stuff in there.'

'Where do I go?'

She opened the door and pointed down the hall. 'First on the left. I'll get the coffee going.'

He filled the sink with hot water, soaked a facecloth and laid it across his forehead. He saw his hand was trembling. I need a drink, he thought. A shot of whiskey. Something to calm my nerves. He sensed the nausea again and for a moment he thought he was going to gag. Then he felt it slowly recede. He soaked the cloth once more, lathered the soap and carefully started to shave.

In the kitchen she had the radio on. A talk show host was discussing extra-marital affairs. A psychiatrist was talking about the male need for reassurance. Megarry took the coffee and felt it warm his throat.

'Are you sure you won't have something to eat?' She

stood with her hand on her hip, a cigarette burning between her fingers. She sounded chirpy. Cheerful almost. How did she do it? She had had more to drink than he had. And after what she'd gone through. The shock of the death.

It suddenly seemed so irreverent. To be standing here in this grimy kitchen drinking coffee with a man she'd only met two days ago, talking like they were old lovers. And McCarthy not yet in his grave. He felt disgust like a cold wave wash over him. For her, for himself, for the whole damned sordid business.

'No. This is all right.' He stood awkwardly nursing the coffee cup, trying to find a means to get decently away, back to work. She tapped some ash into the sink and fiddled with the radio.

'I hate these talk shows,' she said. 'Yappety yappety yap. Let's find some music.'

Megarry tried to smile. He gulped the black coffee. She got a station playing rock and roll. 'My heart stood still' a voice crooned against a background of guitars and drums. He knew that song.

'That's better,' she said. She sat down at the table and poured more coffee. 'Refill?' She held the pot out and Megarry extended an unsteady hand. 'Feeling better?'

'A bit.'

'You need a drink,' she said and held her finger up. 'A real drink.'

'It's too early,' Megarry lied.

'Hair of the dog. You should try it.'

'I have to go.'

He sat the cup down and moved away from the table. She came across and put her arms around his neck. He smelt the warm feminine smell, the fading scent of last night.

'I won't see you out. They might talk.' She nodded slightly towards the hall and then put her mouth forward to be kissed. 'You were good,' she said. 'Great.'

'You too.'

At the top of the stairs she leaned over the banisters and whispered, 'Keep in touch.' She said it in a perfunctory way as if she didn't really mean it, as if it was just something to say. He realised she was dismissing him.

On his way across town he ran into traffic, rows of cars and lorries banked up because of the security checks near the city centre. As he bent to knock on the radio, he noticed that his hand was shaking again. He gripped the steering wheel in an effort to steady it. At the same time he became aware of a tightness in his chest and a difficulty breathing. He glanced in the mirror and saw how dishevelled he looked. In his haste he had forgotten to comb his hair. There was a nick on his cheek where he had cut himself shaving and the blood had congealed into an ugly red blob. He rubbed it with his fingers but only made it bleed again.

The traffic had slowed to a crawl now and the heat inside the car was becoming unbearable. He started to sweat, the shirt sticking to his skin, small waves of odour reaching his nose when he moved his arms. He wished he had showered in that woman's flat, brought a fresh shirt. But how was he to know? He hadn't planned anything. He wound down the window in a frantic effort to get some air.

After a while he got behind a cattle truck coming in from the country. He could see the black snouts of the animals pressed tight against the rails, hear the rattle of their hooves on the boards, the terrified screams every time the truck lurched forward, as if they knew what awaited them at the journey's end. The noise seemed to burrow into his brain, the screams of the cattle and the roar of the traffic further up the road. He started to close the window again. His hand was worse now, the tremor causing the glass to rattle. The thought struck him that he was trapped inside the car. He felt the perspiration stream down his forehead and into his eyes, burning like salt.

A fit of panic seized him. In desperation he drove off the road at the first turn and parked in a side street.

He needed a drink. A shot of whiskey. There was a bar he knew not far from here. He locked the car and started to walk quickly along the street, past shoppers and pedestrians, careless now about his safety, wanting only to reach the pub.

The place was almost empty. There was a handful of civil servants from an office nearby drinking coffee, and an old man with a dog, reading a paper by the bar. He ordered a large Bushmills and topped it up with water and waited till the barman was out of sight before gulping most of it down. He put more water in and played with it for a while, then polished it off and ordered another. He took this one to a seat near the window where he could think.

The bar was gloomy, the light playing tricks with his eyes. He stared round the room. The civil servants sat in a huddle, heads conspiring over the coffee cups. He turned to where the old man had been sitting and his heart stopped. The man was gone. He must have slipped out. In his place another man leaned forward, his hands gripping a heavy revolver, preparing to fire.

Megarry closed his eyes. Jesus Christ, he thought, I'm going mad. He thought of his father, of McCarthy's cold face on the mortuary slab, of the hairs sprouting from his nostrils. He felt a cold sweat break once more across his forehead. He lifted his glass and drained it. When he looked again, the old man was bending to stroke the dog. He saw Megarry and smiled.

Megarry leaned back and waited for the nausea to pass. He counted the seconds till he began to feel better. He found he could breath again. After a while the shaking stopped and the pain in his head began to ease. It was replaced by a warm feeling, a sense of normality, and the faint stirrings of hunger. On the bar, in a glass case, were a number of unappetising sandwiches, probably there from yesterday, the bread curling at the edges. He got up and went to the bar and ordered one, and with it a pint of Guinness.

The civil servants were on an early break. He listened to them nattering on about some problem that had arisen in the office. One of them was threatening to involve the union. He watched her, a thin nervous young woman with black hair swept back in a bun. She did most of the talking. 'It's his attitude,' she said. 'His attitude is wrong. He's got an attitude problem.' The others kept nodding in agreement. 'He interferes. He thinks he knows better. That's what gets me. He thinks he knows better than me and I'm doing the job.'

'That's right,' another one said. 'He thinks he's an expert. He's got this way of making you feel incompetent.'

Megarry found himself thinking of Mrs Clancy – Marion, call me Marion – thrashing about in the sheets in that cramped little bedroom. How had that happened? He must have been drunk. Tired and then the whiskey.

He felt the remorse return and on impulse decided to ring Kathleen. He finished the sandwich and the drink and made his way out to the hall.

The moment she came to the phone he caught the

concern in her voice. 'I rang you this morning. Did you get my message? They said you were out.'

He tried to cover his confusion. 'I had to see someone, so I didn't go in direct. Any news? How's Jennifer?'

'That's what I was ringing about. I was talking to Crowley.'

'Yes?'

'He says she's better.'

'How better? What did he say? Is she eating anything?'

'A small bit. Scrambled eggs. That sort of thing. He says she's making progress. She slept well.'

'There,' Megarry said. 'I told you she'd be all right.' He felt a surge of elation.

'Maybe,' Kathleen said.

'No maybe about it. She'll be okay. When can I see her?'

'I don't know. Crowley has to decide.'

'Should I ring him?'

'No. Leave it with me. I'll talk to him. I'll let you know.'

'What if I went up there?'

'Don't do that,' she said quickly. 'Just leave it. I'll get back to you.'

'All right,' he said reluctantly. 'Kathleen?'

'Yes?'

'Try not to worry. It'll work out. Trust me. You'll see.'

'She misses you.'

'I'll get up there as soon as he lets me in. Okay? Keep in touch.' He was about to put the phone down when something struck him. He started up again, carried forward on a wave of goodwill. 'Maybe you and I could have a bit of dinner. Somewhere nice. It would help to lift you out of it. Somewhere quiet. What do you say?'

She hesitated before replying. 'Maybe, Cecil. Let's not rush things.'

'No, I mean it. It would be good for you.'

'Like when?'

'Give me a day or two.' He knew at once it was the wrong thing. 'Kathleen? You're still there?'

'Yes.'

'I mean it about dinner.'

'Just ring me when you're ready, Cecil.'

'In a day or two.'

He heard her put the phone down. He pushed down the hall and out into the street. It was filling up with shoppers, window-gazing in light summer dresses. He headed north, up Royal Avenue towards the Bank of Finance, his mind a jumble of emotions.


Mr Maguire was the manager. He turned out to be a fat man with small eyes and a striped waistcoat and the air of someone who was very busy. He came bustling out to meet him and brought him into a little office with pictures of former bank directors and a silver golfing trophy in a glass case.

'What can I do for you, Mr. . .?' he studied some papers on his desk. 'Superintendent? How do I address you?'

'Mr is fine.'

'Well then, Mr Megarry, what can I do for you?' He sat back in his chair and sucked his teeth with an odd swooshing sound.

'David Stewart? He had an account with this bank.'

'Did he?'

'Yes. I'd like to know more about it, if that's possible.'

Maguire raised a hand. 'Well, now. Before we proceed. You realise there is confidentiality involved. This isn't normal.'

'I appreciate that,' Megarry said. 'But I'm conducting a murder enquiry.'

Maguire considered. 'I see.' He leaned forward and pressed a button on a console. There was a buzz and a woman's voice came on the line. 'Heather? Can you see if we have a file on a Mr David Stewart.' He looked across the desk. 'What's his address?'

'Glencraigie.'

'Glencraigie. Can you bring it in to me if you find it?' He sat back and sucked his teeth again. 'What happened to him?'

Megarry shifted in his chair. 'He was shot dead three days ago.'

'Ah,' Maguire said. 'I remember it now. I didn't connect him. Terrible business. Terrorists?'

'I don't know. We're still making enquiries.'

Maguire nodded sympathetically. 'You people are certainly kept busy.' He seemed to run out of conversation. He tapped the desk impatiently and then suddenly brightened up. 'We had a raid here a few years ago. Your men were very helpful. Recovered all the cash. We were naturally delighted.'

'I'm pleased.'

'Yes, indeed. I won't hear any criticism of the police.'

There was a shadow at the door and a middle-aged woman in a grey suit came in. She left a bundle of papers on Maguire's desk and bent to whisper in his ear. Megarry caught her sneaking a look at him before straightening her jacket and leaving.

'Now,' Maguire said. 'David Stewart.' He leafed through the papers. The police chief saw his eyebrows raise. 'He'd a lot of money with us.'

'Thirty-two thousand pounds.'

'How did you know that?'

'Just information I picked up.'

Maguire put the file down and studied the police chief anew. 'What exactly do you want from me?'

'I want to know how the account came to be opened. What arrangements he had with the bank. Whether he gave you any instructions. How he made the lodgements. Where the money was coming from. Anything that can help me with this business.'

'It's highly irregular.'

'I'm just looking for your co-operation.'

'I might have to go to the board. We don't normally give out this kind of detail. It's all strictly confidential.'

'I could use other channels,' Megarry said. 'Get a court order for disclosure. It could be messy. It would look like you were obstructing our enquiry. You might not want that.'

Maguire's face flushed. He looked agitated, like a man who wasn't used to being put under pressure and didn't like it much. 'All right. Have you got a pen?' Megarry slipped a notepad from his pocket. The manager flipped open the file again.

'The account was opened in July 1989 with an initial deposit of three hundred pounds.' Maguire turned some pages and glanced up at the police chief. 'From then on he made regular deposits of various sums up to a thousand pounds until two weeks ago.'

'How were the payments made?'

Maguire consulted the file again. 'Cheque, cash.'

'Did he leave any particular instructions with you?'

'No. The money was simply lodged in his account. It's a special interest account.'

'Did he make any withdrawals?'

'Yes.' He ran his finger along the page. 'December 15th

1989, five thousand pounds; January 20th 1990, five thousand pounds; March 14th 1990, twelve thousand pounds. Am I going too fast?'

'No,' Megarry said and continued writing into the notebook. 'Cheques or cash?'

'Cheques.'

'Would you have a record of those transactions?'

'We might have,' Maguire said.

'What I need is names. Who was lodging the money. Who received the cheques he withdrew. I take it they'd be made out to the recipient?'

'It could be either. They could be personal cheques.'

'But you'd have records?'

'We should have,' Maguire said. He closed the file suddenly as if he had already divulged too much.

'When do you think you could get me the information?' Megarry said.

The bank manager pursed his lips. 'I'll have to get clearance. Providing I get that, I could have it to you in a day or two. Maybe tomorrow.'

Megarry stood up. 'I don't suppose you know where this money was coming from? He was only a farm labourer.'

Maguire's face became solemn again. 'No,' he said. 'We never ask questions like that. That's none of our . . .' He suddenly realised what he was saying. 'I mean . . .'

'I know,' Megarry said. 'Confidentiality. I understand.'

Harvey was on the phone when he pushed open the door. He tossed his cigarettes across without speaking and gestured for Megarry to take a chair.

'Umph,' Harvey said into the mouthpiece. He nodded his head vigorously and stretched his lips so that his teeth gleamed. 'Umph,' he said again.

Megarry lit a cigarette and waited. After a while Harvey put the phone down and leaned forward across the desk.

'Sorry about that. It never stops. What can I do for you?'

'Did the forensic report come in yet?'

Harvey's face brightened. 'As a matter of fact it did. This morning.' He started to rummage among the papers on his desk.

'Does it tell us anything?'

'Not a lot we didn't know.' Harvey pulled a folder from under a pile of boxes and flicked it open. 'The weapons used to kill Stewart were an Armalite rifle and a Kalashnikov. That's consistent with the injuries. Neither weapon has been used before in any murder that we have files on. They found cartridge cases and fragments.'

'What about McCarthy?'

'Browning .9 millimetre pistol. You knew that already.'

'Had the weapon been used before?'

Harvey looked over the top of the file. 'It doesn't say.'

'What?'

'It doesn't say. Here. Read it yourself.' He handed the report across the desk.

'Surely they carried out tests?'

Harvey spread his hands. 'I've no doubt. It's routine. But there's nothing in the report.'

The police chief let his eye travel down the page. 'Who wrote this?'

'Bob Donaldson. The same guy who did the preliminary.'

Megarry tapped his fingers on the desk. 'Maybe I should talk to him. I've another case. Man called Clarke. He was killed about eighteen months ago.'

'And?'

'Whoever killed him also used a Browning.'

Harvey sat back and stroked his chin. 'Well now.'

'Interesting isn't it? Two deaths, similar circumstances, same weapon. Maybe I should see the forensic report on the Clarke case.'

The phone rang. Harvey grabbed it. 'Control.' He made a face. 'Just a moment.' He held the instrument out. 'For you.' The police chief took the phone and pressed it to his ear.

'Mr Megarry?' He recognised the voice immediately.

'Yes.'

'Fleming here. I've been trying to reach you.'

'I've been busy,' Megarry said abruptly.

'I want to have a look at the forensic report. I understand you have it.'

'That's right.'

'Can I see it? Can you send it across?'

Megarry took a deep breath. 'No,' he said.

Harvey looked up quickly. There was a pause on the line, then Fleming was back, his voice throbbing with anger.

'Are you refusing me access?'

'Yes.'

'This is preposterous.'

'It's a police matter, Mr Fleming. You've no right to the report.'

'I've every right. I serve on the security committee.'

'Nevertheless. This is privileged information. I can't let you have it.'

'I'll take this up with the chief constable.' His voice was rising and he was almost shouting down the line.

Megarry tried to stay calm. 'You go ahead and do that.'

'It's outrageous. You're being obstructive. I need to see that report.'

'Why?'

'Because I'm not happy with the way you're handling this case.'

'I'm sorry about that.'

'The Commander will hear about this.'

'I'm sorry about that, too.' There was another pause. He could hear Fleming's heavy breathing. 'Is that all Mr Fleming?'

'No it's not. You're going to regret this.'

'What?'

'I'm going to have you removed from this case.'

# 9

Megarry and Nelson took up position near the cemetery gates, hidden from view on a slip road behind a clump of trees, where they could watch the funeral procession without being seen.

The police chief had been here before. He wound down the car window and checked his watch. It was ten to three. He unbuckled his seat belt and turned to Nelson.

'Tell me about the McClenaghan uncles.'

'There's not a lot to say. They run the farm together, three of them. Sort of co-operative, although the eldest brother seems to be the boss. I've checked with the local cops and they're clean as a whistle.'

'Never been in trouble?'

'No. There was some brouhaha last year. It seems the eldest guy, Samuel, has a reputation as a Romeo. A young woman mysteriously found herself pregnant and said he was responsible. There was hell to pay.'

'Nothing new in that.'

'Maybe not. But that's bible-belt country. Fornication is severely frowned on. It's the sort of thing you get stoned to death for.'

'It better not catch on,' Megarry said. 'What's their name?'

'Beattie.'

'All single?'

'Yes. There's also the mother. She's getting on a bit. Nearly seventy. She runs the house, cooks, that sort of thing.'

'Any pastimes? Apart from chasing women?'

'They raise greyhounds. It's a profitable sideline. And Samuel's in the RIR.'

The police chief turned and stared. 'Is he now? That's interesting. Part-time soldier?'

'Very part-time. He goes out with them a couple of times a month. I think he's just in it for the money.'

'You didn't tell the cops why you were interested?'

'I just said I was making routine enquiries.'

'We'll have to talk to them,' Megarry said. 'We'll go out there this evening and hear what they have to say for themselves.'

There was a bustle of activity at the bend of the road, and the funeral came into view, a straggling band of ill-dressed mourners, preceded by a black hearse. They seemed to be mainly poor people, friends and neighbours of the dead man. A figure in a top hat and overcoat stood out from the rest, walking in front, carrying in his hand a pair of folded gloves.

At the cemetery gates, the procession stopped and the man in the top hat began giving directions. The coffin was removed from the hearse and a tricolour flag spread on top. Four young men stepped forward and the coffin was hoisted onto their shoulders. Megarry craned to see. Probably McCarthy's sons. Or maybe nephews. Relatives anyway.

A priest had appeared from somewhere, a small bird-like figure in a flowing white surplice, accompanied by an altar boy. A tall man with red hair emerged and there was a quick consultation before a guard of honour formed up on either side of the coffin.

Megarry studied their faces. He recognised some of them immediately: Billy McCann, Frank Delaney, Tommy Johnson, old comrades from former campaigns, come to pay their last respects. At one time or another, in the past thirty years, McCarthy had helped to put them all away. Little did they know they were burying a traitor.

The priest had produced a prayer book and was starting to read aloud. There was a brief flurry of hands as people in the crowd blessed themselves. Then a momentary hesitation before the funeral moved off again, the priest out in front and the altar boy struggling with a heavy crucifix on the end of a long pole.

They went in through the cemetery gates, the immediate family first and then friends and neighbours. Megarry wound down the window to get a better view. He watched as they filed slowly past, pale faces and ill-cut clothes, about a hundred people altogether. Some of them he recognised as old Republicans, but most were unknown to him. He searched the procession, looking for the man he had come to find.

Near the tail of the cortege he saw him; a broad figure in a dark suit with a black mourner's tie. George O'Connor, one of the first people McCarthy had betrayed. Mrs Clancy was right. George hadn't let him down. He hadn't changed much. The same boxer's face, only older and fuller. The same stocky build, same broad shoulders. Despite the advancing years he looked a figure of authority, someone to command respect. The police chief watched as he drew level with the cemetery gates. For a moment he looked up and Megarry thought he had spotted them, but it was only to observe the clouds gathering now in the pale sky.

There was a roll of thunder and a scattering of raindrops. O'Connor pulled his collar up and bent to whisper to a small man with glasses, who walked beside him. In a moment they had passed into the cemetery and the procession was gone.

Megarry turned to Nelson. 'A military funeral. I'm impressed. And there must have been a hundred people there. Not bad for a guy who was practically down and out.'

'What does it mean?'

Megarry thought for a moment. 'It means he still had some clout with the movement, otherwise they wouldn't have sanctioned it. They don't give that type of funeral to just anyone. Certainly not to an informer. And definitely not to an informer they've just killed.'

'Maybe they're just being clever? Maybe it's just a camouflage?'

'I don't think so. It's real enough. The only things missing are the shots over the coffin.'

'What do we do now?' Nelson said.

'Wait. Give them time to bury him. They'll be out again. Then we'll nab our man.'

Megarry looked at the rain, running now in streams across the windscreen. He reached out and knocked the wipers on. 'Have you noticed how it always rains at funerals? It's my abiding memory, standing in the wet by a muddy graveside and the water running down my neck, while some sky-pilot drones on about what a great guy he was.'

He switched the radio on. A band was playing traditional music, a haunting air on pipes and fiddle, a lament. It seemed ironic that while McCarthy was being laid to rest, the BBC should play a lament. Across the road a rifle peeped from sandbags around an army post. The traffic had started to flow freely again. Megarry sat back and waited.

They began drifting out in ones and twos, small knots forming impatiently on the roadside, waiting for the widow to emerge so that they could make their final gestures. She came at last, sodden and grief-stricken, a small woman surrounded by a cluster of supporters, her black coat shining in the rain. Megarry noticed how frail and insignificant she seemed, grey hair wrapped in a dark scarf, old beyond her years. She didn't look at all like the virago Mrs Clancy had described.

He watched as O'Connor detached himself from a group of mourners and walked quickly towards her. He hugged her close for a moment, patting her wet hair as if she was a child. Then he bent to whisper in her ear.

He turned to the rough youths standing awkwardly in their damp suits and shook their hands. He paused for a moment, his duty done. More mourners approached. O'Connor muttered some more words and then wheeled sharply and began to walk down the road, his hair plastered against his forehead in the pouring rain.

'Right,' Megarry said. 'Go.'

Nelson started the engine. Ahead of them, on the pavement, O'Connor hurried along, anxious to reach the shelter of the nearest bus-stop. He kept his eyes on the ground, his suit collar pulled tight against his neck. Nelson drove slowly past and then stopped. Megarry pushed the back-door open and took a deep breath. When O'Connor was almost abreast of them, he stepped out.

'Can I give you a lift, George?'

O'Connor peered at him through the rain. 'Do I know you?' he said.

'I think we've met, George. Get in the car.' Something in the voice warned O'Connor. He turned quickly and started to retreat but Nelson was already behind him.

'Do as you're told, George, and nobody'll get hurt.' He pulled O'Connor's arm up his back and forced him down onto the seat. Megarry slipped in beside him and jammed the revolver into his ribs.

Nelson drew the curtains in the interview room and plunged the place into darkness. He knocked on a switch and the bulb cast a pool of light down onto O'Connor's chair. His suit was crumpled because of the rain. He didn't move or speak, just sat staring ahead as if oblivious to what was happening around him. Nelson walked back into the shadows and sat down at a desk beside an old-fashioned tape-recorder.

After a while they heard footsteps. The door opened and Megarry was in the room. He looked at O'Connor for a moment and then came and stood beside him.

'Remember me, George? Cecil Megarry. I need some information.' He found his cigarettes, shook the packet loose and held it out. 'Smoke?'

O'Connor said nothing.

Megarry lit a cigarette and put the packet away. He pulled over a chair and sat down. 'I'm investigating John McCarthy's murder. I think you can help me.'

O'Connor's eyes flickered momentarily in the blinding light but he made no effort to speak. The police chief sat back into the shadows.

'I knew John well in the old days. Before all this recent

stuff started.' He tapped out some ash. 'You were a good friend of his. You stuck by him. I admire that. Friendship is a valuable thing.'

O'Connor made no response.

Megarry waited for a moment, then started again. 'I'm trying to be civilised, George. We're all reasonable people here. There's no need for anyone to get excited if they don't want to. But you have to understand. I have a job to do. I want to know what John was up to lately. These little trips he was taking. Where he was going. What he was doing. I take it you were aware of them?'

O'Connor sat still, his hands folded now in his lap. Megarry observed him. On his forehead little beads of sweat had appeared.

'Why don't you tell me? You'll have to tell me in the long run. Why not tell me now and get it over with?' He blew out smoke and it hung in the air in a blue cloud around the light bulb. O'Connor blinked again as if the smoke was hurting his eyes. 'No one's going to blame you, George. I'm not asking you to inform. All I want to know is what John was up to before he got killed. That's all. You might help us find his killers. Nobody even has to know.'

He watched O'Connor, seeking a sign that he understood, that he might co-operate.

'It happens all the time, you know that. People talk all the time. You don't have to feel any the less about them.'

In the background they heard Nelson cough.

'Look,' Megarry said. 'You want us to find his killers, don't you? You want us to find the people who shot him. I know it wasn't your crowd. So who did it? I won't rest till I find out. Why don't you help me?'

O'Connor bit his lip and turned his eyes towards the police chief. His mouth moved and for a moment he seemed to teeter on the brink of indecision. Then he switched his gaze away again, ignoring Megarry, the room, Nelson, retreating back into his shell.

Megarry suddenly stood up. 'All right, George. You're forcing my hand. You're leaving me no option.' He walked to the back of the room. There was a silence except for the steady breathing coming from the chair. O'Connor had lowered his face and was staring at the floor.

Megarry cleared his throat and started again. 'George, I'm going to tell you some things you may not want to hear. Some things you won't like. I'm going to shatter some of these notions you have about John. He wasn't everything you might have thought. Did you know he was an informer?'

O'Connor's eyes blinked and his head turned just an inch.

'John worked for me for years. Right through the fifties and sixties. He gave me lots of information. Important stuff. Arms dumps, safe houses, people. He put away Delaney, Johnson, Burns, all your old pals.' He moved back and sat again in the shadow. 'I can prove it. I can show you receipts for payments. I can tell you things that could only have come from John. I know the houses that Reilly used when he was on the run. I know the woman he was seeing. There was only a handful of you who knew that information.'

O'Connor suddenly moved his head. He stared out beyond the pool of light, seeking to find Megarry's face.

'It's true, George. It's not very pleasant but it's true, nevertheless. He was an informer. He betrayed the whole lot of you. Why do you think I'm so interested in him, for God's sake?' He took a deep breath. 'He betrayed *you*.' The only sound was the scraping of Megarry's chair as he moved closer. 'He did, George. He betrayed you. Fourth of April, 1959.'

O'Connor gave a cry. 'You're lying.' He tried to get out of the chair, struggling towards Megarry. In a moment Nelson was on his back, pinning his arms. 'You're lying! You're making it up!'

'He did, George. I'm sorry. I can prove it. He gave me the dope to put you away.'

'No!'

Megarry reached into his pocket and pulled out a wad of documents. 'Let me show you something.' He leaned towards O'Connor, the papers spread open in his hand. 'This is an authorisation of payment. Look at the date. Look who it's made out to. Look who signed it.'

O'Connor turned his face away. 'It could be forged.'

'It's not forged. It's real. Here. Examine it.' He pushed the documents forward again. 'Go on look at it. See for yourself.'

O'Connor slowly reached out his hand.

At that moment there was a sharp tap at the door. Nobody moved. Megarry turned quickly and looked at Nelson. His face had gone white with rage. The tapping came again.

'Jeeesus,' Megarry said.

Nelson got up at once and walked to the door. There was a few muffled words and then the detective was back, bending over Megarry and whispering in his ear.

'What?'

Nelson shrugged in a hopeless gesture, and spread his hands.

Megarry got up and paced to the corridor outside. A young policeman was waiting. He was fidgeting with a ballpoint pen. 'Well?'

'There's a phone call for you, sir. I told them you were busy but they insisted. Said it was urgent.' He tried to apologise, twisting the pen nervously in his hand.

'What name?'

'Maguire, sir. Bank of Finance. He said you'd know what it's about.'

Megarry cursed. The bank manager's sense of timing was deplorable. He followed the policeman along the dark corridor and up the stairs to the operations room. The place was like an ant heap, detectives rushing around, phones ringing. In a corner a radio was blaring messages to patrol cars. The phone was lying awkwardly on a desk. Megarry lifted it up and cupped it to his ear, trying to block out the noise. 'Yes.'

It was a bad connection. The voice seemed to be coming from far away. 'That information you were seeking. I'm having problems.'

Megarry felt his temper rise. 'What sort of problems?'

'I had to go up the line. I explained that to you. I'm meeting some resistance. They say it's confidential.'

Megarry felt his patience snap. 'Look, Mr Maguire. You tell your Board or whoever it is, that I'll be in court first thing in the morning seeking an order of disclosure.'

The bank manager started to argue.

'I'm going right now to inform every newspaper editor in town. I'll make sure this gets banner treatment. You're obstructing a murder investigation.' Megarry's voice was rising. 'And what's more, if it turns out that any of this money has been gained illegally, I'll instigate proceedings against you for criminal conspiracy. Now you go and tell that to your Board.' He slammed the phone down.

O'Connor was sitting where he had left him. He looked up and swallowed hard so that his Adam's apple bobbed. Megarry sat down beside him and tried to catch his breath.

'Tea?'

The man nodded. Megarry turned to Nelson who got up and left the room. Megarry took out his cigarettes. 'Here,' he said. He struck a match and held it out. While O'Connor bent into the flame, the police chief started again.

'Look I'm not interested in what you guys are up to. Not now, anyway. I'm interested only in this particular case. I want to find John's killers. So I'm not asking you to inform.'

O'Connor raised the cigarette and inhaled deeply.

'What were all these trips about? Where was he going? What was he doing? He was working for somebody wasn't he? Who was he working for?'

O'Connor looked into Megarry's face. 'We thought he was working for you.'

'For *me*?'

'For the police.'

'He wasn't working for me. I haven't seen him for twenty years. What makes you think he was working for me?'

'These trips, the money. We suspected he might be touting.'

'So what did you do?'

'We kept him under surveillance for a while. But we could never prove anything.'

'Did your people kill him?'

O'Connor shook his head. 'No. Not us. We'd no reason to kill him. We'd no evidence against him.'

'You're telling me the truth?'

'Sure. We'd nothing against him. He wasn't involved with us. And he was drinking too much. He was too unreliable.'

'So what use would he be?'

'Not much. It would only be gossip he'd pick up in pubs.'

The door opened and Nelson came in with a mug of

tea and a bag of sugar with a spoon sticking out of the top. He set the mug down beside O'Connor.

'What sort of gossip?'

O'Connor shrugged. 'Sympathisers. Members of Sinn Fein. Maybe houses.'

'And you were aware of this?'

'We were suspicious.'

'Was he ever interrogated?'

'Not officially. I took him aside and warned him that some of the lads were asking questions. I was hoping he'd get the message. You know, drop whatever he was doing.' He lifted the tea and spooned in sugar.

'When was this?'

'About six weeks ago.'

'And what was his reaction?'

'He denied it. He said the trips had to do with odd jobs he was doing up the country.'

'And you believed him?'

'I wanted to.'

'Why?'

'Because he was an old friend. I felt sorry for him. He'd been through a lot of trouble. Marriage problems, drink. I stick by my friends.'

'Even if they're touts?'

O'Connor lowered his eyes. 'That was never proved.'

'How often did you see him?'

'A couple of times a week. I used to give him money from time to time to help him out.'

'When's the last time you saw him?'

'A few days before he died. I met him in a pub down the town.'

'Did you arrange to meet him again?'

'Yes.'

'When?'

'The night he was killed.' He lifted the tea. Behind him, Nelson had the tape-recorder running.

'Tell me about it.'

O'Connor rubbed his hand across his mouth. 'He said there was somebody he wanted me to meet. Some fella he seemed to think could be useful to us.'

'In what way?'

'I don't know. He was very vague. He said this guy had a line into information that could be important. But he wasn't specific.'

'Where were you supposed to meet?'

'He wanted me to see him in the Clock Bar in Divis Street. He said he'd take me to meet this man. I made an excuse and said that wouldn't suit. Between ourselves, I wanted more control over the situation. I wanted to be able to use my own car. He came back later and changed the plan.'

'Where to?'

'Glencraigie Crossroads.'

'What?' Megarry suddenly stood up so that he was towering over O'Connor. 'What time?'

'Eleven o'clock. I told him that didn't suit so he changed the time to one. He said if I was delayed not to worry. He'd wait for me. He seemed very anxious for me to go.'

'Was this other man supposed to meet you at Glencraigie or were you going somewhere else?'

'I don't know.'

'Weren't you suspicious about meeting someone like that in the middle of the countryside at one o'clock in the morning?'

'Of course. That's why I didn't go in the end.'

'And you know that's where he was murdered?'

O'Connor lowered his eyes. 'Yes.'

'Do you think this man you were supposed to meet might have killed him?'

'Who knows? Maybe there was no man. Maybe it was just some notion he got into his head. Maybe he thought it might help him back into our good books.'

'But *somebody* killed him. And this other man, Stewart. Somebody murdered them. What's the connection? Did he ever mention Stewart?'

'No. I never heard of him.'

'What about the name Bobby Rossi? Mean anything to you?'

'No.'

'Thomas Clarke?'

'No.'

Megarry sighed and gestured to Nelson to knock the tape off. They heard O'Connor speaking again. 'What was it all about? What do you think?'

The police chief paused. 'I think you're a lucky man to be alive.' He knocked the light-switch off and pulled the curtains across. Daylight flooded back into the room. 'You must be hungry. We'll get you something to eat.'

As he was moving to the door, O'Connor stretched a hand out and detained him. 'What you said earlier about John. You said be betrayed me. Was that true?'

Megarry looked at him. He was asking for something, seeking reassurance. Why shatter his faith? What good would the truth do for an old man like him? He shook his head. 'No,' he said. 'That was just something I made up.'

He left Nelson with the tape and went back up to his office, feeling a dark mood begin to settle on him. He had always hated interrogations; the way they broke men, forced them to betray their beliefs. It was a dirty business, just as the whole craft of special branch work contaminated all it touched. There were times when he thought he hated it; the spying, the manipulation, the compromises, the dark world of touts and informers, bags over the head, lonely deaths on country roads. But it was all he knew. He had given his life to it and he had been successful. But he knew in his heart that it was like holding back the tide.

O'Connor, Johnson, Burns: one by one he had put them away over the years with McCarthy's help, and one by one they had been released. Now they were recruiting new people, planning new campaigns. He was tired now and McCarthy was dead.

The office was deserted, the files from last night piled in an untidy heap on Nelson's desk, the air dank with the smell of countless cigarettes. He sat down, pulled open the drawer and took out the bottle. He held it up to the light and then poured a shot into a coffee mug. Just a jigger. It would help him to think.

He suddenly remembered that he'd had nothing to eat all day apart from the sandwich in that bar where he'd rung Kathleen. He'd have to stop this, get some order into his life. He swirled the whiskey in the stained mug and knocked it back, feeling it warming its way down into his gut. He'd have to find some way back to Kathleen. He would have to slow down, make time. And Jennifer. At the thought of his daughter he felt the guilt return. He had neglected them. For what? His career? A vendetta as Kathleen had said? Whatever it was, it was all turning to ashes.

He searched his desk till he found the piece of paper he was looking for. He lifted the phone and started to dial.

As he did so something caught his attention. He

smoothed the paper out and paused, fingers poised over the phone.

'Yes?' a voice said.

Megarry stirred himself. 'I'm sorry to bother you like this.'

'Ah, superintendent.' Prescott's voice sounded warm and encouraging. 'How's your enquiry going?'

'So, so. I've hit a snag. That's what I'm ringing about. I wouldn't have bothered you, but you did offer to help.'

'Of course. What can I do?'

'I'm having a bit of trouble. With Fleming.'

'Ah,' the voice said. 'We need to talk about this. When are you free?'

'Right now,' Megarry said.

# 10

Prescott's office was in a heavily-fortified building out near Dundonald with views over rolling pastureland and the soft contours of the Castlereagh Hills. Megarry remembered when it had housed the Department of Agriculture and a different army of foot soldiers had clogged the approach roads at five o'clock in the evening as the lights began to go out in the grey windows.

He showed his ID to a weary squaddie in a sentry hut and waited while he raised the security boom, then drove up the steep incline and parked in front of the entrance hall.

Prescott was waiting for him in the foyer and led him into a book-lined study dominated by a massive desk, stuffed with drawers and loaded with baskets for filing papers and reports. Pinned to the wall above the desk was a huge map of the city, coloured in green and blue, with little red flags indicating army positions.

'Drink?' Prescott hovered in front of a cabinet and pulled

out two glasses. Megarry hesitated. He'd had several drinks already, and on an empty stomach.

'I'll have a whiskey. Small one.'

'Any preference?'

'Bushmills, if you have it.'

'Of course,' Prescott said. 'Ice and water?'

Megarry nodded. He ran his eye along the bookshelves. They were mostly military textbooks. Several were histories. One caught his attention, *The Battle for Stalingrad*. Prescott came and stood beside him and handed him a glass.

'Second World War. It's a hobby. Are you interested?'

'No more than the next person,' Megarry said. 'I remember being evacuated down to Fermanagh. Running wild in the countryside. It was fun.'

Prescott smiled and the lines around his eyes creased. 'I missed it. It was a fascinating war. Particularly the Eastern Front. That's where the war was actually won. It was a turning point.' He sounded animated. 'The Russians never get proper recognition. In Stalingrad they had to fight street by street, house by house. They took horrendous casualties, but they stopped the Germans. The winter did the rest. After that, the war was really over.'

Megarry nodded politely.

'That's my one big regret, missing that war. Soldiering is about fighting don't you think? And that was a real war, fought over continents, ideologies. What we've got here isn't a proper war. Shooting people in the back of the head.'

'It's real enough,' Megarry said. 'For those caught up in it.'

'It's just a squabble. A dirty little dogfight. You know we could put this thing down in two weeks if we were allowed to do it? Take out the leaders, the organisers. The guys who sit back in safety and direct operations.'

'That's easy to say. It's different if you have to live here.'

'But I do live here.'

'Permanently, I mean.'

'Yes, permanently.' Prescott's face broke into a serious smile. 'This is my home now. My life is here. I expect to die here, be buried here.'

'I thought . . .'

'No, here. My wife is in England. We didn't get on. The children are all grown up. Why not here?'

'You've no roots.'

'I've got commitment.' He waved a free hand towards the window and Megarry could see the broad expanse of countryside, a thin mist clinging to the green outline of the hills. 'This is my home.' Megarry thought Prescott was going to continue but he suddenly stopped and took Megarry's arm and led him to the desk. 'You didn't come here for this. Tell me about your problem.' His voice had gone soft, inviting confidence. He sat across from Megarry and clasped his hands together. The police chief took a deep breath.

'I got a call today from Fleming. He wanted the forensic report on the Glencraigie murders. He's been after me for days. I refused.'

Prescott nodded but didn't say anything.

'He got quite abusive. Said he wasn't happy with the way I was conducting the inquiry. Anyway, things got a bit out of control. He threatened to report me to the Commander and the chief constable. In the end he said he'd have me taken off the case.'

'That sounds like Fleming,' Prescott said. 'Not the most subtle, is he? But I wonder if it was wise? To refuse him, I mean. After all he is on the security committee.'

'It's a matter of principle. He's not involved in this inquiry. We don't normally share information like this. And I'm not convinced he's genuinely interested. I think he just wants it to score points.'

Prescott frowned. 'But surely you can't withhold information.'

'I can,' Megarry said.

'He'll get it anyway, if he goes over your head. It'll just make you look obstructive.'

'But why should I cut a stick to beat myself with? If I give him the report he'll be back at the next meeting wanting to know why I didn't do this or that. Why I didn't follow this line or that line.' He lifted the whiskey and took a gulp. He could feel his anger beginning to stir and he tried to stay calm. 'I can't work like this. I can't have constant interference. I've got to be free to conduct the inquiry the way I think best. I can't have busybodies poking their noses in all over the place.'

Prescott nodded.

'There's also the question of precedent. I've never had this kind of thing before. It was almost like a directive. If I give in this time it'll simply leave the way open for more of the same. I'll never be able to conduct an inquiry in peace.' He realised his glass was empty. Without saying a word, Prescott took it from him and went back to the cabinet and recharged it.

'Is that it?' he said.

The police chief lowered his eyes. 'I'm serious about this.'

'I can see that.'

'If I'm taken off the case, I'll resign. There'd be no point carrying on.' There was a silence while the two men observed each other across the desk.

'It won't come to that,' Prescott said at last and put his

glass down. 'Let's consider the options. How well is the case going? Are you making any headway?' He suddenly sounded businesslike, almost abrupt.

'It's up and down.'

'Tell me.'

Megarry sighed and began to outline the facts. When he had finished, Prescott said: 'This man McCarthy. You say you knew him. How well?'

'It was years ago. I'd lost touch.'

'And you say he was an informer?'

'Yes.'

'Well maybe that's why the IRA killed him. It seems obvious.'

'No,' the police chief said. 'It's not that simple.'

'Why not? They kill people for informing, don't they?'

'It's just a feeling I have. It's too neat. I don't like it.'

'Have you questioned anybody?'

'Lots of people.'

'Any chance of an arrest? Anything that would satisfy the security committee, keep them quiet?'

The police chief shook his head. 'I could haul in the usual suspects. But I'd have to release them again. I don't want to play games. I want to solve this thing.'

Prescott toyed with his glass while he considered. 'All right,' he said. 'We'll tell them that the case is at a delicate stage. That you're on the verge of a breakthrough. I'll talk to Fleming. Leave it to me.' He seemed to relax, the problem solved. He pointed to Megarry's glass. 'One more? For the road.'

Megarry pushed the glass across. 'Go easy. I have to drive.'

Prescott brought the fresh drinks and sat down again. He massaged his chin. 'There's something I should tell you.' He immediately raised a finger. 'Now don't get upset.' He paused and Megarry watched him across the desk. 'About two years ago we had a very interesting case. Theft of weapons from an army base in North Antrim. About forty or fifty items were taken. They were nearly all Brownings.'

'What happened?'

'We arrested a serving soldier. RIR member. He admitted collusion.'

'I don't remember it.'

'You wouldn't. He was never charged.'

Megarry sat forward in his chair. 'Why not?'

'It was decided not to press charges. He was dismissed of course.'

'But why? It's normal to charge them isn't it?'

'Security considerations. Bad publicity. Bad for morale. To be perfectly blunt, it was too bloody embarrassing.'

'So it was covered up?'

'Afraid so,' Prescott said. He lifted his glass and looked a little sheepish. Megarry felt the anger stirring again.

'Why wasn't I told about this?'

Prescott waved his hand. 'Not my decision. You'd have to go further up the ladder, I'm afraid.'

'And what did he do with the weapons?'

'Sold them.'

'To Loyalists?'

Prescott sighed. 'No,' he said. 'This is the really embarrassing bit. He sold them to the IRA.'

'Jesus.' Megarry set his glass down.

'Look,' Prescott said. 'I told you not to get upset. It's all water under the bridge. It's best left alone.'

'Where is this guy? Can I talk to him?'

Prescott was shaking his head. 'Too late for that, I'm

afraid. He shot himself. Two weeks after he'd been dismissed.'

Megarry sat back in his chair. He felt stunned by what he had just heard. 'This is incredible.'

'Look,' Prescott said. 'You mustn't mention this. If word gets out, it'll come straight back to me. There's only a handful of people know about it.'

'But it's outrageous. Who advised this decision?'

Prescott sucked in his cheeks. 'Our friend Fleming.'

Megarry stood up. He could feel a trembling begin, a rage about to overtake him. It confirmed all his worst beliefs about the security committee, the whole nest of military dilettantes who sat in judgment on him. 'I've heard enough,' he said. 'I'd better go.'

Prescott came round the desk and put his arm across his shoulder. 'Just get on with the case. You're doing good work. And leave Fleming to me. I'll handle him.' He began to fuss with some papers, clearly embarrassed.

Something occurred to Megarry. Something he should have thought of, and it caused his anger to melt away. He remembered what Nelson had told him outside the cemetery. Beattie was in the RIR and he lived near Ballymena. He held out his hand. 'Thanks for seeing me.'

Prescott had started to apologise again.

'Put it out of your head. Not a word to anyone.'

Beattie's farm was set in rugged hillside, about fifty acres of sheep and cattle. They found it in half an hour driving around the roads of North Antrim, after getting directions in Ballymena. As they pulled into the farmyard a black collie came barking to meet them. The noise brought a man in overalls from behind a barn. He had a young woman with him, a thin athletic type, who leaned against a tractor and watched the policemen as they got out of the car.

Megarry caught the smell of manure. The man came forward, slowly rubbing his hands on his overalls, a cautious look on his face.

'We're police officers,' Nelson started. 'We're looking for Samuel Beattie.'

Megarry saw the woman glance quickly towards the man. He thought her face looked frightened.

'That's me.'

'Can we talk to you for a minute?'

'What about?'

'David Stewart.'

The answer seemed to throw him. He hesitated and then regained his composure. 'Sure,' he said. 'I won't be able to tell you much. I hardly knew him.'

The dog was growling at Nelson's feet. The man called it to heel, slipped a noose around its neck and tied it to a post. 'You'd better come into the house.' He turned to the young woman. 'Wait for me, Annie. I won't be long.'

He led them across the yard to a white-washed bungalow. At the door he scraped the mud from his boots and rubbed his hands again on his dungarees in a casual way, then led them into the kitchen.

An elderly woman was sitting at a table with a child, reading from a book. She looked up when the policemen came in.

'I've got some business, Ma. I'm taking these men into the parlour.'

The woman ignored them and continued talking to the child. Beattie pushed open a door and led them into a small room stuffed with bits of furniture.

'I didn't do it.' He closed the door and motioned for the policemen to sit down.

'Do what?'

'Murder that oul bastard. Isn't that what you're here for?'

Megarry studied him. Thirty-four, thirty-five; small, wiry hands red and calloused from working in the fields all day. He'd be strong, the police chief thought. Beneath the slight appearance there would be an underlying toughness.

'Nobody said you did. Just tell us what you know about him.'

Beattie sat down and stretched his legs in a nonchalant pose. 'I know what he did to Julie.'

'Nothing was ever proved against him.'

He smiled with one side of his face, a sort of lop-sided defiance. 'That's just because that bloody inspector and him were in cahoots.'

'So you've no sympathy for him?'

'Not a lot.'

'He got what he deserved?'

'I didn't say that. But don't ask me to feel sorry for him.'

'He's better off dead?'

Beattie shrugged. 'Probably. At least the kids in Glencraigie are safe.'

The policemen exchanged glances. Megarry started again.

'How well did you know him?'

'Not very well. I told you.'

'He was a farm labourer. You must have bumped into him from time to time.'

'Oh, I used to see him around all right. He drank in Mooney's in Glencraigie, but I never bothered with him.'

'Anything else?'

Beattie pursed his lips. 'He came here once trying to sell me stuff, but I chased him. That was before the business with Julie. If I'd known then what I know now he'd have moved a bit faster, I can tell you.' He smiled again and let his eyes drift to the corner of the room. A double-barrelled shotgun stood propped against the newly-painted wall. 'I use that for shooting vermin,' he said.

Megarry suddenly felt tired of the conversation. Beattie was playing games. 'That's dangerous talk.'

'What's dangerous about it?'

'We're conducting a murder enquiry.'

'So? Am I a suspect?'

'You could talk yourself into becoming one.'

Beattie laughed. 'I've an alibi,' he said. 'I was working that night.'

'With the RIR?' Nelson asked.

'How did you know that?'

'We've made enquiries.'

'Well, then. You know all about me. I was on patrol the night he was killed. Don't take my word for it. It's easily checked.' He folded his arms across his chest and watched them defiantly. 'Anything else you want to know?'

'Had he any enemies?'

'Loads of them,' Beattie said. 'Me, for one.' He laughed again and Megarry suddenly had an urge to slap his face.

'Anybody who'd want to kill him?'

'Who knows? Maybe the father of some other kid he was abusing.'

'Anybody you know?'

'No,' Beattie said. 'Not offhand.'

'Do you have a personal weapon?'

'Yes.'

'What type?'

'Browning pistol.'

'Can I see it?'

Beattie smiled once more. 'You won't catch me that

easily. I check it in. I don't need to bring it home. I've that boy there.' He nodded again to the shotgun.

'Look,' Megarry said suddenly. 'You're not being helpful.'

'Why should I be helpful?'

'We want to find who murdered him.'

'So why should I help you? Whoever did it, did a good job as far as I'm concerned.'

Megarry sighed.

'What was he trying to sell you?' It was Nelson this time. Beattie turned quickly to look at the detective. 'You said earlier he came round here selling something.'

'Oh, that was just animal stuff. I think he'd some sort of line in animal stuff.'

'What sort of stuff?'

'Cattle drenches, growth promoters. I didn't ask him. I ran him, like I said. Anyway, I don't deal with these travelling salesmen. Anything like that I need, I go to the vet.'

'I thought he was just a labourer?'

'He was a labourer, but I think he dealt in these things on the side. Sort of a nixer.'

'We've been told he was a bit simple,' Megarry said. 'Was that right?'

'When it suited him. But there were no flies on the same boy. He was cute enough.'

'Where are your brothers?' Nelson suddenly asked. 'You've two brothers, isn't that right? Where are they?'

'They've gone into town. They should be home shortly. Do you want to talk to them, too?'

'Possibly. Do they feel the same way you do about this business?'

'More or less.'

The police chief stood up. 'We'll have to go. We may

want to see you again.' At the door he stopped. 'How long have you been in the RIR?'

Beattie studied him, suspecting a trap. 'Three years.'

'Based locally all the time?'

'That's right.'

'What do you know about an arms theft?' He saw Nelson glance at him.

'Arms theft? Beattie said, rubbing his chin. 'Where?'

'At your base.'

'First I've heard about it. When was it?'

'About two years ago.'

'No,' he said. He shook his head. 'That's news to me.'

'Do you know anything about one of your colleagues killing himself?'

Beattie looked confused. 'Are you making this up?'

'No.'

'I never heard of that. Anything like that happened, I'd hear about it. What's he supposed to have done?'

'Shot himself,' Megarry said.

Outside in the yard the young woman was still working on the tractor. She looked up and waited for Beattie to join her. Across the fields, lights were coming on, shining like pins against the dark hills.

Beattie stopped at the car and leaned on the window, the dog yapping at his heels. 'This arms theft. What was taken?'

'Mainly pistols,' Megarry said. 'Brownings. Just like your personal weapon.'

Nelson started the engine.

# 11

He woke with a stabbing pain in his chest, like someone had tightened a belt across him while he slept. When he put his hand to his forehead it felt hot and moist. He lay for a while in the narrow bed, feeling the damp sheets clinging to his skin, the stinging sensation in his toes and ankles spreading upwards when he tried to move. He closed his eyes and the pain pressed down on him like a vice.

He knew at once that this was more than the usual brooding hangover. He thought of the dizzy spell he'd had the night Kathleen rang to tell him about Jennifer, and later the panic attack in the car on his way from Mrs Clancy's flat. What's happening to me? he thought. What's going wrong? Why is my body letting me down?

He considered ringing for a doctor and then as he lay in the sheets, trying to decide, he felt the pain slowly recede and in its place a dull ache that throbbed its way throughout his frame. He struggled out of bed and made his way into the bathroom and leaned into the enamel sink, trying to retch. But all that came was a thin spew of mucous, stained brown from the previous day's drinking.

He sat for a while on the side of the bath listening to the water gurgling in the cistern until he felt well enough to go into the kitchen. He found some aspirin in a cupboard. In the fridge were a few eggs and a half-eaten loaf of bread. As he plugged in the kettle to make coffee, the phone rang.

Even before he answered it he knew it was Kathleen. She sounded brisk and businesslike as if she was going to take no nonsense. His first impulse was to tell her how bad he was, and then it occurred to him that she might think it was just another excuse. So instead he gripped the phone and prayed that they wouldn't fight.

'I'm leaving shortly for the hospital. Do you want to come.' He caught his breath. 'I talked to Crowley and he says you can visit. I'm leaving now. You asked me to tell you.'

As he bent his head, he felt the pain starting again. 'How soon? Before she's out, I mean?'

'He's not giving any dates. You know what they're like. But she's on the mend.'

'That's good.'

He could hear her waiting. 'Do you want to come? We can go in together. She'd like to see you.'

'Well.'

'Don't tell me, Cecil. You're busy.'

'No. It's not that.' He started to apologise.

'It's all right. I understand. Maybe some other time. I'll tell her you're too busy to come and see her.'

What he feared, had happened. He was making her angry. 'Wait,' he said. The kettle was boiling, a shrill whistle piercing from the kitchen. He went back and knocked it off. 'Where will you be?'

'In the car park. Do you know how to get there?'

'Should I bring her something? A present maybe?'

'No,' she said. 'Just bring yourself.'

It was a grim Victorian pile, high walls, security gates, grey granite buildings. He knew as soon as he entered that this was no ordinary place. The hospital itself was behind a belt of sycamore trees, hidden from the road, as if to shield it from public view.

She was waiting as she said in the car park and he didn't recognise her at first. She wore a silk scarf, despite the warm day, and dark glasses. The first thing she said was: 'You're looking dreadful.'

He tried to change the subject. 'What is this place?'

'It's a psychiatric hospital.' She saw him wince. 'It's not as bad as it sounds. It's quite modern. It used to be an old mental hospital, but it's been refurbished.' They were walking along a grass verge and his shoes sunk in the soft lawn. 'I want to warn you. She doesn't look great. Be prepared for a shock.'

'How bad?'

'Bad enough. There were days when she wasn't eating at all, but she's coming round. She's lost a lot of weight.' He looked at her and saw the lines around her mouth begin to tremble. 'I've been worried, Cecil. This hasn't been easy. It's just so . . . so irrational.'

'What does Crowley think?'

'He thinks she'll be okay.'

'That's not what I meant. Why is she doing it?'

'They don't know. It could be anything. It's common in young women her age.'

He stopped and laid a hand on her arm. 'Tell me honestly. It's me, isn't it? She's doing it to punish me.'

She tried to look away. 'You'll have to ask Crowley.'

'For neglecting her. For not being home. For being a bad father.'

She stopped. 'Who knows? She doesn't know herself. She's disturbed. Nobody knows.'

'But she's getting better?'

'Yes. It'll be slow. But Crowley says she'll get there.'

He felt a sudden surge of relief, as if he had done some terrible deed and been absolved. Kathleen had started walking again.

'Don't blame yourself,' she said.

Ahead they could see a modern building with a black roof and glass panelled doors. A middle-aged woman in a matron's uniform was sitting behind a desk writing in a ledger. She looked up and smiled when she saw them. 'Good morning. How are you this morning?' She had a cheerful voice and bright bird-like eyes.

'This is my husband.' Kathleen turned to Megarry and the matron stood up and grasped his hand.

'Jennifer's good this morning. She had breakfast. She's going to be just okay.'

'Can we see her?'

'She's sleeping. Taking a little nap. But you can see her. Go on down. You know where to go.'

They started down a corridor with wards on either side. In some of them Megarry could see people dozing. In one room a fat woman in a pink dressing gown sat knitting in a chair. She lifted a ball of wool and waved when she saw them pass.

They stopped outside a door and he felt Kathleen press his hand. The room was still except for the deep breathing coming from the crouched figure in the bed. There were flowers and a couple of get-well cards on a little dresser, books and a bottle of Lucozade. He suddenly felt inadequate, standing there empty-handed. He should have brought her something.

He bent over the crouching figure and saw that it was just as he had imagined. Her face had shrunk, dark circles beneath the closed lids, her thin hair spread like gossamer on the pillow. She lay in a tiny bundle, her knees drawn up towards her chest, as if she was a child. He felt something inside him start to break.

He turned away. Kathleen reached out a hand and touched the sleeping face. She came awake at once. For a moment she didn't recognise him. He saw her blink and then awkwardly she pulled herself up.

'Dad,' she said. Her voice sounded hoarse. She stretched her arms to kiss him.

All at once he buried his head in her hair. He tried to speak but only a mumble came. He held her, his hands gently caressing her face till at last he let her go. 'Forgive me,' he said. She tried to smile, the sleep still in her eyes. 'Forgive me for what I've done.'

She looked at Kathleen and then back again at Megarry. 'I'm getting better. Look at me. Don't you think I'm getting better?'

'Of course. But you have to eat. Tell me what you had for breakfast.'

'Porridge, scrambled eggs, toast.'

'Did you eat it all?' He found himself talking as if she was a child.

'Well, not all.'

'But most. You ate most?'

She smiled again. 'Most.'

'That's good. That's the only way you'll get better. You need nourishment.'

'Are you sleeping all right?' Kathleen said.

'All day long. I just feel so tired.'

'That will pass,' Megarry said. 'As you build up your strength. But you have to eat. Remember that. You must eat.'

'I will. I promise.'

'We want you fit and well. We want you home.'

'When?'

'Don't you like it here? All this fussing?'

She turned her pale face to him. 'But it's not home.'

'I know.' He patted her hand. 'We'll get you out as soon as possible. It's up to you. You have to get better. You have to eat.'

There was a knock and a young nurse put her head round the door. She had a clipboard in her hand. 'Hello,' she said. 'How is Jennifer this morning?' She came bustling into the room, the starched uniform cracking as she moved. Megarry stood up.

'We'll go.'

'It's all right. This'll take only fifteen minutes. You can wait if you like.'

He glanced at his watch. 'No,' he said. 'I'd better go.' He bent and kissed Jennifer gently on the cheek. She clung to his neck.

'You'll come again?'

'Of course. Tomorrow. What would you like me to bring? Your most favourite thing?'

She laughed, a thin hollow sound from her chest. 'Surprise me,' she said.


Kathleen walked with him to the car park.

'Are you going to stay?'

'Yes. I think I'll wait. I want to see Crowley.'

'She's grand. What do you think? Don't you think she looks well?' He stared at her, seeking her agreement.

'Slow down,' Kathleen said.

'She's grand. She'll be out in no time.'

'Don't rush. These things take time.'

'But she's getting better. Everyone says so.'

'Yes, she's getting better. But it might be a while.'

He stopped and took her hand. 'I'm sorry. Honest.'

'It's all right.'

'I never meant it.'

'I know, Cecil. You're not a bad man. You just don't think.'

He settled into the driving seat and wound down the window. She touched his sleeve.

'Take care of yourself.'

'Why do you say that?'

'You don't look well.'

'I'm just tired. I need a rest.'

'Take it easy,' she said.


He drove north out of the city, up into the steep hills above Ligoniel and then into the flat countryside around Templepatrick. The whole way he thought of Jennifer, his mood swinging between elation and guilt. He tried to convince himself that she was recovering. She was eating again and Crowley was looking after her. Those were big pluses. Crowley was a clever old bird who'd dealt with this before. He knew the tricks, knew what to watch for. If anyone could get her better, it would be Crowley.

Then an image of her crouched in the hospital bed would overwhelm him, the sunken eyes, the grey, deathly pallor of her cheeks, and he was plunged again into remorse. He had caused this by his neglect, as surely as if he had starved her himself. The times when she had needed him he'd been away, working late at the office or out drinking with buddies at the Montrose Hotel. He'd been a bad father, a bad father, a bad . . .

He stopped at a coffee shop near Antrim and forced himself to eat a breakfast of bacon and eggs. The pain he had felt this morning had eased, although he still found difficulty getting his breath. He sat for a while at a window seat and looked out onto the street, thinking of what Prescott had told him about the arms theft. Fleming had advised a cover-up to save embarrassment and no one had thought to tell him. He knew why. He didn't count.

He remembered Kathleen's words, 'What thanks do you get?' They repaid him by undermining him, belittling him, obstructing him. By making sport of him at the security meetings. They treated him like some colonial hick, a bumbler who didn't know what he was doing. The thought infuriated him. He understood this province better than any of them. He was born here, had roots here. He'd been dealing with it all his life.

Glencraigie village was deserted when he arrived, apart from a few stragglers playing Dominoes in the sun outside the pub. At the war memorial a couple of old men sat on a bench and gossiped. He drove past the police station and out towards the railway tracks, only slowing down when he approached Stewart's cottage. The door was slightly ajar and, across the road, he noticed Nurse Bradley's car. She saw him pull in at the gate and came to meet him, her thin face tight with displeasure. She blocked the door, her arms folded across her chest.

'She's sleeping. You can't see her.'

'I won't disturb her.'

'She's had a terrible few days. We had the funeral yesterday. She can't take all this stress. She should really be in hospital.' She struggled to keep her voice low, but it still grated on his nerves.

'It's all right,' Megarry said. 'I just need to check something in Mr Stewart's room.'

She stood aside reluctantly to let him pass. 'Well then. Be careful. Don't make any noise.'

The house was quiet. The sun filtered in through the window and cast a shadow on the table with the bottles and medicines. A fire was still burning in the grate. Nurse Bradley followed him in.

'Where is she?'

She pointed to the bedroom. 'I'm warning you now. Don't disturb her. The creature's exhausted.'

Megarry pushed open the door to the second bedroom. There was a fresh smell. The window was open and all the clutter was gone, the books, the clothes. Someone had tidied it up. He turned quickly to the nurse. 'There were some things there. Beside the bed. Where are they?' The urgency in his voice alarmed her.

'I threw them out.'

'Where?'

'The place was a mess. How that poor man was able to live like that.'

'Where did you put them?'

'In the bin.'

He pulled open the kitchen door. In a tiny yard a black plastic bin stood beside a pile of boxes. A ginger cat scurried away and watched from the safety of a wall. Megarry pulled off the lid. Nurse Bradley hovered beside him.

'Was it something important?'

He ignored her and began spilling out bits of rubbish, bottles, discarded waste, till they lay in a pile at his feet. Near the bottom of the bin the sun glinted on glass. He reached down and drew out a jar. It was the same one he had noticed at Stewart's bedside. It was coated with a white powdery substance. He raised it to his nose and sniffed.

'Did I do something wrong?' Nurse Bradley said.

Megarry slid the jar into his pocket. 'No,' he said. 'You were quite right. The place stank. It needed a good cleaning up.'

He had arranged to meet Nelson in a car park near the city centre, a dark underground cavern which he used sometimes for rendezvous. The detective was waiting. As he saw the car pull in he opened the door and got in quickly beside Megarry. He looked nervous.

'I don't like this place. It gives me the creeps. A man could get murdered here and no one would ever know.'

Megarry ignored him and drove up the ramp and out into the midday traffic.

'Where're we going?'

'Delhi Street. Clarke's widow. You know it?'

'Springfield?'

'That's right. No-man's land. We won't be hanging around. In and out, as the sailor said.' He turned to the detective. 'You carrying?' Nelson pulled his jacket back. The butt of a revolver peeped from a shoulder holster. 'When we get there, I want you to get into the driver's seat. Keep the engine running. If you see anything dodgy, give the horn a blast. I won't be long. Fifteen, twenty minutes.'

They were passing along the Falls Road. Near the junction with the Royal hospital a huge mural covered a gable wall. An IRA man and a Palestinian linked arms and pointed rifles to the sky. POWER COMES FROM THE BARREL OF A GUN, a slogan read. And beside it: OUR DAY WILL COME.

Megarry swung the car right onto the Springfield Road, past the sandbagged police station, rifles poking from a sentry box. About half a mile further on he turned right again into the sloping valley of the estate.

Before them, row after row of drab little boxes twisted like snakes, right up to the foot of the mountain. A pall seemed to hang over the rooftops, a fine mist of rain and smoke from a hundred chimneys. Near the shopping centre a gang of kids played football on the road. They stopped to watch the car go by, then bored, returned to their game.

Megarry drove along Delhi Street, counting the houses till he spotted number twenty-three. The front door was open, the curtains in the window pulled aside to make room for a large potted fern. He drove on up the street and turned and came back again. Apart from a man pushing a bicycle there was no one about. He stopped and glanced around once more, then stepped smartly out.

'Keep the engine running. Any sign of trouble, bump the horn.' He pushed the gate open and walked quickly up the little drive. An ugly black labrador watched from the pavement. Megarry grabbed the knocker and banged hard. There was no response. He started again and then heard a movement somewhere inside the house.

The door opened and a tired-looking woman put her head out. 'What is it?'

'Mrs Clarke?'

'Yes?'

'Police, Mrs Clarke. Nothing to be alarmed about. I just wanted to ask you a few questions about your husband.'

'What about him? He's dead.'

Megarry looked quickly over his shoulder. If he stood chatting like this on the doorstep, he would attract attention. 'Could I come in? It'll only take a few minutes. I'd prefer to talk to you inside.'

She stood undecided, and then slowly backed away, the weight of authority forcing her to retreat inside the house. Megarry followed and closed the front door.

The woman was already trying to explain. 'He wasn't involved in anything. I've already told that to the detectives from the barracks the first time they came.'

Megarry examined her. She was about forty-five, small, mousy hair. Over a flowered cotton dress she wore an apron splashed with gravy stains.

'It's all right, Mrs Clarke. I just need some information.'

'He was just an ordinary working man. He minded his own business. He was just trying to earn a living. He was involved in nothing. Honest.' She pulled a grubby handkerchief from the apron and began to sob.

He glanced around the little room at the cheap furniture, the cracked oilcloth on the floor. His eyes rested for a moment on the Republican calendar above the fireplace with the oval picture of a dead IRA man: 'In Proud and Loving Memory.' It didn't mean anything. They all had them now.

He put a hand on her shoulder. 'I need to ask a few questions.'

'Is it about the compensation?' She started to cry again, dabbing at her eyes with the handkerchief.

Megarry put his hand into his pocket, searching for his cigarettes. So that's what's bothering her, poor devil. Gently he lifted her head and put a cigarette into her hand. As he lit it, he smiled. 'Have a claim in?'

'Yes. I've four kids, mister. It's hard.'

'And you think you'll be disqualified if he was in the IRA?'

'He wasn't. Honest to God. He was in nothing. The neighbours'll tell you.'

'I believe you, Mrs Clarke.' He pulled on his cigarette. 'Trust me. I've no interest in your compensation claim. God knows, you need all the money you can get.'

She was twisting the handkerchief, rolling it into a ball. 'He was in nothing, sir. Honest.'

Megarry patted her hand. 'That's not what I'm here for. I'm here to find his killers. You can help me.' He paused. 'There's too much of this. Too many innocent men like Tommy taken away and killed. Too many widows and orphans. Will you help me? Will you answer a few questions?'

Slowly she nodded her head.

'Did he ever leave home at all? Go away for a few days? Anything like that? Think hard now. It's important.'

He saw the answer in her eyes before she spoke. 'Yes.'

'Tell me about it.'

'We used to fight over it. Well, not fight, just argue. It's stupid now that he's gone, God rest him. But you know the way it is sometimes.' She smiled for the first time, her mouth spreading in an unconscious grin. 'I was a wee bit jealous.'

Megarry smiled back and patted her hand again. 'That's only natural. Tell me more. When did it begin?'

'About eighteen months ago. He just came in here one Friday afternoon. He sat down there and had his tea and then he tells me to pack a bag because he's going away for the weekend. Well, I wasn't one bit pleased. He'd never done anything like that before in all the years we were married. But he said it was all hush hush and he couldn't say any more but not to be worrying because he'd be back in time for work on Monday morning. He was a milkman, you know.'

'I know,' Megarry said.

'I wasn't too happy about it, but what could I do? I hardly slept a wink with worrying all weekend. But sure enough on Monday morning about five o'clock I hears this car stopping outside the door, and the next thing he's in the kitchen as right as rain and ready to eat a horse.'

'Go on.'

'So, I got his breakfast ready and while I'm making it I'm busy trying to find out what he's been up to. But he wouldn't tell me. Just kept saying that the whole thing was very confidential and he couldn't say nothing, but I wasn't to get worried because there was no danger involved. Well, nothing more happened till about five or six weeks later when he comes in again, in the middle of the week this time, and tells me the same story. He has to go off once more, but he's squared it with the foreman and there'd be no wages lost.'

Megarry nodded.

'I tell you, my heart was broke with worry about it. You know the way it is yourself. I kept thinking the worst. But I just kept my mouth shut and said nothing and prayed it would stop. I'll always remember the last trip he made. It was the week before he got killed. He was very excited about it. I asked him what had him so happy and he smiled and said this was it. The last time. He said he'd be gone for a few days and when he got back that would be the end of it. There'd be no more. He asked me how I was fixed for housekeeping money and then he gave me a big bundle of notes, about two hundred pounds. And to tell you the truth, that only made me worse, for I was sure now he was up to no good.

'He was away altogether about three days and he came back as usual, fit as a fiddle. It was a Sunday morning and when he came in he said he was tired and went straight up to bed and didn't get up again till the middle of the afternoon. That was the last trip. A few days later he was dead.' She was sobbing again, the crumpled handkerchief pushed tight against her eyes. Megarry squeezed her shoulder.

'I'm sorry, Mrs Clarke. He was a good man. I don't think he was doing anything wrong.' He stubbed out the cigarette. 'Tell me about how he was killed.'

She sniffed and dabbed her eyes. 'It was a few days later. He came in after work and said he had to go out again to meet someone. I asked him was it to do with the trips but he wouldn't say. He just said he had to pick up some money. Well, he never came home alive. Five days later they found him out near Carrickfergus. He'd been shot.'

'Did he take a bag with him that time?'

'No.'

'Did you tell this to anyone else. About the trips?'

She shook her head. 'A couple of detectives came round when he was killed. But I was afraid. I thought they might try to make out he was in the IRA and get my compensation stopped. So I didn't tell them.'

'How many of these trips did he take altogether?'

'Oh, maybe a dozen.'

'How often?'

'Every five or six weeks.'

'When he was away did he ever get in touch with you? Did he ever write or phone, make contact in any way?'

'No.'

'Did anyone ever contact him before the trips? Any phone calls, notes, letters? Anything like that?'

'No. Nothing. We've no phone, anyway. The nearest one's in the kiosk at the bottom of the street, but the kids have it broke all the time.'

'Well how were these trips arranged? How did he know when to go?'

She stared at him. 'That's a good question. I never figured that out.'

'Was there anyone he associated with? Any particular pal?'

'Not really. He didn't go out much. Maybe the odd pint from time to time. And a wee trip to the bookies. He liked a flutter on the horses.'

'Did he ever mention a man called John McCarthy?' She shook her head. 'David Stewart?'

'No.'

'Bobby Rossi?'

Her mouth trembled for a moment and then she threw her head back and laughed till her body shook. 'It's not Bobby,' she said. 'It's Barbara.'

Megarry stared. 'Barbara?'

'God forgive me, I shouldn't be laughing like this. I made the same mistake myself. I thought it was some fancy woman he'd got. At his age. But it's not a woman at all. It's a man. And he's been dead for years.'

Megarry's mouth fell open. 'What do you mean?'

Mrs Clarke wiped her eyes. 'We had a right old row over it. "Who's this Barbara Rossi?" I said. He got very angry. "You've been going through my pockets." "Indeed and I have," I said. "Do you think I'm going to sit here like an eejit and you out gallivantin' for days on end with some fancy woman. Who is she?" I said. And God have mercy on him, he just sat there and smiled. "It's not a woman, Mary," he said. "It's an old dead king. Barbarossa." "And what's it got to do with you?" I said. "That's private," he said. "Has it got to do with these trips?" "It has, Mary. But I can't tell you any more. You'll have to trust me. But I can tell you one thing. It's not a woman, Mary. You're the only one for me." And he gave me a big kiss.'

'Barbarossa,' Megarry said. He grabbed the woman's arm. 'What does it mean?'

She looked startled. 'I don't know. Just what he said.'

'Well, how did you come across it in the first place?'

'In his racing diary.'

'What?'

'I went through his pockets one day, trying to find out what he was up to. I suppose I shouldn't have, but I was worried sick. Well, there it was. Pencilled in. Barbarossa eight pm. Barbarossa nine pm. All over the place. About a dozen times. Different dates.'

'And he told you it was connected with the trips?'

'Yes.'

'Was it a code or something?'

'I don't know. Just what he said. An old dead king.'

'Where is the diary? Can I see it?'

'I haven't got it anymore.'

'Why not?'

'Well, that's another funny thing. When I got all his personal stuff back from the morgue the diary was missing. I got his money and his watch and his wallet. Even his miraculous medal. But the diary was missing. I hunted the house from top to bottom, but I never found it.'

'Maybe he lost it.'

'Maybe. But I don't think so. He took good care of it. It had all the racing information in it.'

'All right,' Megarry said. 'One other thing. Can you remember the first time he went away on one of these trips?'

She wrinkled her brow. 'It was about a week after he was arrested. Let me see. About the middle of January last year. I remember . . .'

Megarry stopped her. 'Did you say he was arrested?'

'That's right.'

'Are you sure? He'd no criminal record. I've checked.'

'Well maybe not arrested. Taken in for questioning. The night the barracks got done. The soldiers went mad that night. They lifted half the men in the district and hauled them in. They were running around like lunatics. He was having a wee drink in Flynn's pub and they just came in and arrested every man in the place. Including the barman.'

'But he got out?'

'The next day. They kept him in the whole night interrogating him. Sure what would he know? He was only a milkman.'

'And you think this was in the middle of January?'

'Whenever the barracks got bombed. Just check the dates. He went off the first time about a week later.'

'You've been very good, Mrs Clarke. Very helpful.' He stood up. 'Just keep this to yourself. This wee visit. It's between you and me. Okay?'

The woman smiled. 'Ah, for God's sake. Do you think I'm mad. Talking to peelers isn't something you boast about around this district.'

'Just you and me. Remember now.'

She reached out her hand. 'There's something you could do for me.'

'Of course.'

'You could help my compensation along.' She started to plead with him. 'Whatever you can do. I've four kids. And just the widow's pension. It's not easy.'

'I'll see. I'll talk to someone.'

Nelson saw him coming down the garden path and waved frantically for him to hurry. Megarry opened the car door and slid in beside him.

'Thank God,' the detective said. 'Fifteen minutes you said. Do you know how long you were in there?'

'I got good stuff.'

'I'm delighted. Let's get the hell out of here.' He revved the engine. 'You were in there over half an hour.' He pulled left at the top of the street past the kids playing on the road.

'Relax,' Megarry said. 'When I was your age I used to walk these streets . . .'

'I know,' Nelson said. 'And the hard men would run when they saw you coming. These days they'd just blow you away.'

# 12

Florentine Avenue was deserted when he arrived. The earlier rain had ceased and a thin sun was struggling through a sky of low cloud. There were puddles in the cracked paving of the pathway and he had to step carefully to avoid getting his shoes wet.

She was surprised to see him. It showed in her face, a withdrawn look, almost furtive as she opened the door, as if she had been expecting someone else.

'Oh,' she said. 'It's you.'

'I won't be long,' Megarry said. 'I just need to check a few things.'

'You'd better come in, then.' She pulled the door wide and stood aside to let him enter. She was wrapped in a faded dressing gown, her bare feet stuck in slippers. He noticed how thin and pale she looked. Her hair was a mess. She saw him looking and said: 'I've been lying down. I haven't been feeling well.'

'I'm sorry to hear that.' He started to follow her up

the stairs.

'It's the shock. It's only sinking in. I have nightmares about it. I keep seeing him in that car.' She led him into the kitchen. 'What a terrible way to die. All that blood.'

'Have you seen a doctor?'

'He'll only give me tablets.'

'Maybe you should.' She didn't reply. Instead, she moved to fill the kettle. He stopped her. 'It's all right. I won't be long.'

She moved some plates from the table and put them in the sink. She was pulling at her hair, trying to make herself presentable. She sat down and took out her cigarettes. 'How was the funeral? Did you go?'

'It was okay.'

'Many there?'

'About a hundred.'

'And the heartbroken widow leading the mourners. What a laugh.'

'Yes,' Megarry said. 'She was there, too.'

'And George O'Connor?'

'Yes.'

'I told you. I knew he wouldn't let him down.' She blew out a wreath of smoke. 'Bloody hypocrite. She didn't give a shit about him when he was alive.'

'That's the way.'

'It makes me sick. Who does she think she's fooling?'

There was a noise behind him. Megarry spun quickly in his chair. The kids stood in the doorway, the smallest one trailing a battered teddy bear. They watched him silently, their eyes wide with suspicion.

'Hey,' Megarry said. 'What's your names?'

The eldest boy glanced towards his mother. 'It's all right,' she said. 'Tell the man your names.'

'Patrick,' the boy said. 'He's Michael.'

'Are you good boys?'

'Yes.'

'Do you help your mammy?'

'Yes.'

Megarry fished in his pocket for change. 'Here,' he said. He pressed some coins into the eldest boy's hand. 'That's for sweeties. Because you're a good boy. He's to get half.'

'What do you say now?' Mrs Clancy said.

'Thank you very much.' They sang it in unison, like something rehearsed, and stood watching her, waiting for directions.

'All right. You can go down to the shop. Hold hands and don't cross the road. And come straight back.' They turned and made a dash for the door.

Megarry smiled. 'They're good kids.'

'They miss John already. Would you believe that? He was better to them than their real father ever was.'

'Look,' he said. 'I'm sorry to have to come back. There's just a couple of things I need to clear up.'

'Like what?'

'Like this name you gave me. You said you got a phone call, remember. You said this man gave you a name. Bobby Rossi.'

'That's right.'

'Could you have got it wrong? Maybe the name was Barbarossa.'

'What's the difference? It sounds the same.'

'There is a difference.'

'I don't know. I can't remember.'

'Come on. Think, Marion. Was it Barbarossa?'

She suddenly got irritated. 'Look. I can't remember these

things. It was a long time ago. One bloody phone call.'

'Was it Barbarossa?'

'Maybe. I thought he said Bobby Rossi. It makes more sense. What does that other name mean? It doesn't mean anything, does it?'

'Oh, it does, Marion. Was it Barbarossa?'

'Yes.'

Megarry sat back in his chair. 'Now,' he said. 'The accent. You said he had an English accent. Are you sure of that?'

'Of course I'm sure.'

'No doubt in your mind?'

She sighed. 'What's all this rigmarole? I told you everything I could. Why are you cross-examining me?'

'You got the name wrong. I want to be absolutely sure about the accent. It's very important.'

'He had an English accent.'

'You know the way sometimes an accent can get distorted on the phone.'

'No,' she said. 'This guy spoke with an English accent. Posh. Upper class. Like you hear in the films. I'm sure of it. Absolutely certain.'

'Okay,' he said. 'I believe you.' He stood up and moved towards the door.

She pulled her dressing gown about her and followed him out to the landing. A door opened downstairs and he saw the bearded figure of the student. Megarry moved to the top of the stairs and then a thought struck him. He turned back.

'How are you doing for money?'

The question caught her unawares. She started to reply.

'Oh, what am I talking about? Here. Get some groceries in.'

174

She opened her hand and looked at the crumpled notes, blue fives, brown tens. In the hallway, he ran into the kids.

'Good boys,' he said. 'You look after your mammy.'

The door banged shut and he was gone.

He ran into Harvey in the corridor as he was coming in. He had a bandage on his right hand.

'What happened?' Megarry asked.

'This?' Harvey held his hand up and clenched his fist. 'I sprained my wrist playing squash.'

'You play squash?' He sounded incredulous.

'Sure I do.'

Megarry examined the stooped, gnome-like figure and tried to suppress a smile.

'What's so funny? I have to get some exercise. Stuck in there all day in that poky little excuse for an office. My doctor recommended it.'

'I didn't know,' Megarry said.

'It keeps me fit.'

'That's good. Look, I need to ask you something.'

'Yes?' Harvey kept his sad eyes fixed on the police chief as if he expected further offence.

'Do you know anything about a weapons theft from a RIR base in North Antrim?'

'When?'

'About two years ago.'

Harvey thought for a moment, then shook his head. 'What did they take?'

'Brownings mainly.' Megarry could see him making the connection.

'No. Never heard anything about that. Tell me more.'

'It was an inside job. They got a guy but didn't charge him.'

'Why not?'

'Damage limitation. They were too embarrassed.'

Harvey laughed. 'I'm sure they were. Yes sir. I'm sure they were very embarrassed.' He suddenly stopped and his face fell flat again. 'It doesn't sound right.'

'I got it from a good source.'

'I tell you what.' Harvey said. 'There's someone I can call. Military police. If there's anything in this, he should know.'

'Be discreet,' Megarry said. 'It's confidential.'

'Of course, I'll be discreet. I'm always discreet.'

He could hear the phone ringing as he came up the stairs. It was Maguire. He knew from the sound of his voice that he had something good to tell. He started off by apologising.

'I hope this isn't inconvenient. I've been trying to reach you all morning.'

'I've been busy.'

'About this information . . .'

'Yes?'

'The Board asked me to call. It seems there's been some misunderstanding. Probably my fault. Anyway . . . we're anxious to avoid court proceedings.'

'I see.'

'I've been authorised to assist you in any way I can.'

'Good,' Megarry said.

'I've some people working on it right now. I can get it over to you pretty soon.'

'Like when?'

'This afternoon.'

'What have you got?'

'Printout of withdrawals from the account. Isn't that what you wanted?'

'Will it show where the money was going?'

'Most of it.'

'What about lodgements?'

'That's more difficult but we're working on that, too.'

'Well, that's very helpful, Mr Maguire.'

'The Board is anxious to facilitate you, Superintendent. In any way we can.'

'I'm delighted to hear it.'

'So, we can assume that you won't be proceeding with this er . . . legal business?'

'If you provide me with the information I require, then naturally, there'll be no need for it.'

'Very good, Superintendent. I'll get it over to you this afternoon. I'll send a courier.'

'Good day, Mr Maguire.'

'Good day, Superintendent.'

Megarry put the phone down and smiled.

He parked the car in a side-street opposite the Telegraph office and walked round to the Central Library. There was a crowd outside; a woman selling fruit from a stall and a boy in a torn anorak waving copies of an evening paper. Megarry glanced at the headlines: SOLDIER SHOT IN KINAWLEY. And beside it: PETROL PRICE TO RISE AGAIN. He pushed through the doors and entered the cool hall.

At once he became aware of an intimidating silence. He looked around. All that glass, all those books, the mock classical pillars, the air of reverence, as if he was in a church. A small man in an attendant's uniform stood to attention beside a statue of a dead dignitary. Megarry approached and the man bent his grey head to listen.

'I'm looking for a reference book. What do I do?'

'Upstairs, sir.' He pointed to a sweeping marble staircase. 'First door on your right.'

The reading room was packed, row after row of inky schoolkids bent over their books, the only sound the rustling of paper as someone transcribed notes.

Megarry made his way to a desk where a couple of librarians busied themselves at a filing cabinet. He coughed gently and a round-faced man in a cardigan looked up at once. He had glasses on the bridge of his nose and a few strands of hair plastered across his forehead. 'Yes, sir.'

'I want to check something? What do I do?'

'Which subject?'

'History, I think. A king called Barbarossa?'

The man pushed his glasses firmly against his face and thought for a moment. 'Barbarossa. Redbeard. No, not a king. Definitely not a king. A Holy Roman Emperor ... or,' His fingers ran across his forehead, toying with a loose strand of hair. 'A Barbary pirate? There were several. Which one do you want?'

The police chief shifted uneasily, suddenly feeling inadequate. The librarian had spread his arms on the counter and was staring directly at him. For an awful moment Megarry thought that everyone in the crowded reading room was listening. He lowered his voice. 'I'm not sure. Maybe you'd have a book that could tell me about all of them?'

The librarian beamed and stood up from the desk. 'I know what you want. The *Classic Encyclopedia*. That should tell you all you need to know about the same gentleman.' He leaned forward again, whispering confidentially. 'Very common name in its day. Europe literally dripping with Barbarossas.' He had become helpful, bustling now to be of assistance. He reached for a pink slip and scribbled some information, then pushed it across the counter towards the police chief, along with a pen on a silver chain. 'Just fill in your name and address and take a seat and we'll get it to you in a few minutes.'

Megarry took the paper, wrote, John Wilson, 38 Sandhurst Gardens, and ventured out into the room. He found a seat at a table near the back, where a freckle-faced girl in a school blazer was writing in an exercise book. She examined him for a moment, stuck a pen in her mouth and then, bored, returned to her homework. He took a deep breath and waited.

After a while he saw a young man emerge with a barrow filled with books and magazines. He stopped when he got to the police chief. '*Classic Encyclopedia*?' He lifted a heavy volume onto the table and brushed his hands, then pushed the barrow away. The schoolgirl was watching again. Megarry pulled his chair in close, bent forward and opened the book.

There was an acrid smell from the paper, page after page of glossy diagrams and charts. He turned to B and began working his way through the columns of heavy type marking the entries: Barbados; Barbara St; Barbarians.

Suddenly his eye fell on it: a figure of a man in flowing pirate dress with a saracen sword in a studded belt. 'Barbarossa. (Redbeard.) Barbary pirate. Died Rio Salado, Africa 1520.' Beneath it was another entry. There was nearly a whole column of them. His finger ran down the page.

'Barbarossa. (Redbeard.) Barbary pirate. Admiral of the Ottoman fleet; Barbarossa Frederick. Holy Roman Emperor. Frederick 1st of Hohenstaufen. Crowned Emperor in Rome in 1155; Barbarossa Operation. Code name used by German High Command for plans to invade Soviet Union during the Second World War.' He stopped and read it again. 'Invasion originally set for May 1941. Postponed till June. Operation aimed to smash Red Army by strike of armoured spearheads into Soviet territory. Regarded by some historians as turning point in the war.'

Something clicked in his head, a half remembered sentence from a polite conversation. He read the text again, slowly this time as the realisation rushed in upon him. He felt a surge of elation. Smash the Red Army: it made a certain sense. He quickly closed the book and stood up.

The librarian looked up as he went past. In the hall a group of students was chattering, smoking cigarettes, out for a break. He rushed by and down the wide staircase.

Out on the street he was suddenly struck with doubt. What if he was wrong? What if it was a mistake? Maybe he was jumping to conclusions, putting two and two together and coming up with six. It could destroy him.

He slowed down and turned the corner into Library Street. The car was where he'd left it, two wheels up on the pavement. Under the wipers, fluttering in the afternoon breeze, someone had left a parking ticket.

# 13

All the way back to the office, he kept turning the information over in his mind. He felt a strange excitement tempered with a sense of danger, the same feeling that he had on the library steps. It was like a foreboding, an instinct that warned him to be careful. The investigation was leading him down dangerous paths. It could backfire. If he was wrong it could bring ruin on his head.

Yet the pieces were beginning to fall into place; the gun, the note in McCarthy's faltering hand, the digits hastily scribbled on a piece of paper torn from a notebook. And the pseudonym. Barbarossa. Smash the Red Army. Particularly Barbarossa.

There was a bundle of mail on his desk.

Some of it Nelson had already dealt with, but one envelope in particular caught his attention. It was marked *urgent* and had the stamp of a courier company. As he reached for a paper knife, the phone rang.

'Superintendent?'

He recognised the voice but couldn't place it. It was soft and polite, like the voice of a supplicant. 'Yes?'

'Donaldson here. That jar you left me. I've analysed it. Interesting stuff.'

'Oh, right,' Megarry said. He pulled his chair closer to the phone. 'What is it?'

'Clenbuterol.'

'What?'

'Clenbuterol. Angel dust. It's a growth promoter for cattle. Strictly illegal. Where did you get it?'

He felt a little frisson of excitement. 'I picked it up.'

'Well that's what it is.'

'Wait a minute. When you say it's illegal, what do you mean?'

'It's banned. Did you get it off a farmer?'

'Well, sort of.'

'Are you planning to prosecute? Very heavy penalties, you know.'

'I don't know yet. Tell me something, is there money in this?'

'You bet,' Donaldson said. 'Big money. It's like heroin. Most of it is cut with other substances. The stuff you gave me is pretty pure.'

'Give me a rough idea.'

'Hey,' Donaldson said. 'I'm just an analyst. You guys are supposed to know these things.'

'Roughly?'

'Good stuff, the kind of stuff in that jar, would fetch anything up to fifty pounds a shot.'

'And what would be in a shot?'

'Look,' Donaldson said. 'I don't know. Ask some of your own people.'

'That jar. If it was full of angel dust, how much would it be worth?'

'I don't know. Fifteen hundred? Two grand?'

Megarry felt his heart begin to thump. 'And how widespread is this?'

'It depends. You get bouts of it and then it dries up. Depends on supply. Apart from being illegal, it can be dangerous to health. But it might be worth it to a farmer who wants to fatten a beast without spending too much on feedstuffs. It's a big temptation.'

'I see,' Megarry said. 'Thank you. You've been very helpful.'

'What about the jar? Do you want me to hold it?'

'Yes, do that. We'll probably need it for evidence.' He put the phone down and lifted the envelope. All of a sudden his chest had gone tight. As he sliced open the envelope, a bundle of paper spilled onto the desk, columns with dates and figures and a scribbled note from Maguire, stressing once more the confidentiality of the material.

He took the paper and examined it. It was a computer print-out of Stewart's bank account beginning on 8 July 1989 with an opening deposit of three hundred pounds. He let his eye run down the page: 8 September, two hundred; 20 September, eight hundred; all deposits, all in cash. Then in October some withdrawals: two hundred on 3 October by cheque, made out to William Baxter. Another on 10 October to the same person, this time for four hundred. In November the deposits started again. Larger sums now, five hundred and six hundred at regular intervals, always in cash. He turned to December and caught his breath. On 15 December Stewart had withdrawn five thousand pounds by cheque. The name of the recipient jumped from the page. He looked again, holding the paper close to make sure there was no mistake.

He bent to the pages, turning them furiously, concentrating on the withdrawals column. The name was there again on 20 January. A cheque had been made out for another five thousand pounds. On 14 March twelve thousand had been withdrawn. There was nothing in April or May. Then in June another cheque and again in July. The withdrawals continued at regular intervals right up to the time of Stewart's death.

He reached for a pen and started over again, slowly this time, logging the withdrawals in two neat columns. When he had finished he made a quick tot. William Baxter had received slightly over six thousand pounds. The other name, the one that excited him, had got twenty-eight thousand. He lifted the phone and tried to steady his voice. Harvey came on the line.

Megarry cut him short. 'Nelson.'

'Of course.' He heard the detective's voice.

'Just drop what you're doing. I need you.'

'What is it?'

'Something's come up. We've got to travel.'

'Where to?'

'Glencraigie.'

Nelson pulled up outside the police station and even before the car had shuddered to a halt, Megarry had the door open and was stepping out onto the deserted street. He saw Blair rushing out to meet them. He came down the steps in a hurry, hands extended in welcome. 'This is unexpected. Why didn't you ring?'

'We hadn't time,' Megarry said.

Blair pushed open the door of the station and ushered

them inside. He pulled some chairs out from the table and waved his hands. 'Tea?'

'No,' Megarry said. 'Not for me.' He was searching for his cigarettes.

'What about you?' Blair spoke to Nelson.

'It's okay.'

'Well then,' the inspector said. He seemed disappointed. 'I was just about to close up. Another ten minutes and I'd have been gone. You should have called.'

'This is urgent,' Nelson said.

Blair turned his attention to Megarry. 'Did I see you this morning? Did you drive past?'

'Yes. I was going out to see old Mrs Stewart as a matter of fact.'

'I thought so,' Blair said. 'I don't miss much. But you were gone before I could be sure.'

Megarry took out a cigarette and struck a match.

'She's not good,' Blair said. 'The shock. I wonder if she'll last? Were you able to talk to her?'

'No. She was sleeping.'

'Ah. Sedated probably.' Blair turned his thin face from side to side, looking at each man in turn. 'So what has you out here in such a panic?'

Megarry sat back in his chair. 'We'd like to talk to you a bit more about Stewart. Clear up a few things.'

'Sure,' Blair said. He sat closer to the table. 'Fire away.'

'We'll start at the beginning. You told me he was a farm labourer?'

'That's right.'

'Doing occasional casual work. Drawing the dole from time to time. No other means of income.'

'You asked me all this before.'

'I know I did. I'm asking you again.'

'No,' Blair said. 'No other means of income.'

'You're sure?'

'As far as I'm aware. If he had I think I'd know. It's difficult to keep a secret in this neighbourhood.'

'But sometimes people have secrets?'

'Sometimes. They usually come out in the end.' He gave a little smile.

'All right,' Megarry said. 'Let me ask you something else. Are you familiar with clenbuterol? Do you know what it is?'

'Sure I do. Angel dust. It's an animal drug. They use it for fattening cattle.'

'Is there much use of it around here? Do you come across it from time to time? You know it's illegal?'

'Of course. I get the odd case. Now and again. It's hard to detect. You have to catch them with the stuff. By and large I wouldn't say it was a problem.' He paused. 'Why do you ask?'

The police chief took a deep breath and his belly heaved. 'I believe Stewart was dealing in it.'

'What?'

'Yes. That's what I was doing out with Mrs Stewart this morning. I found a jar with traces of white powder. I had it analysed. The report came in this afternoon. It was clenbuterol.'

'Maybe there's an innocent explanation.'

'Maybe. I saw the jar the first time we searched the house. It was in his bedroom. But I didn't connect it.'

'Well, I'll be damned,' Blair said. He pulled at his wedding ring. 'Old Davy pushing angel dust.' He shook his head from side to side.

'I also found this,' Megarry said. He pulled out the bank book and set it down on the table.

'What is it?'

Megarry studied the inspector's face. 'It's a bank account. In Stewart's name. He had thirty-two thousand pounds in there when he died.'

'Thirty-two thousand? You're kidding?'

'I'm not,' Megarry said. His face was composed, his eyes watching the inspector. 'Go ahead. Read it for yourself.'

Blair lifted the book and quickly turned the pages. Then he set it down again. 'It's incredible. No possibility of a mistake?'

'I've checked with the bank. It's his account all right. They've confirmed it.'

'And you think he got this money from selling angel dust?'

'Unless there's some other explanation. He was ideally placed, going from farm to farm. Who would suspect him? He was simple, wasn't he? You told me that.'

Blair sat back in his chair and rubbed his chin. Suddenly he sat forward again. 'Do you think this is linked with the murder?'

'I don't know. But it was a nice little racket. If he hadn't been killed, I suppose it could have gone on for ever.'

Blair gave a little sigh. 'I have to hand it to you guys. This is going on right under my nose and it takes you people to crack it. Boys a boys.' He shook his head. 'You're dead right. Who would have suspected him? Thirty-two thousand pounds. To look at him you wouldn't think he had tuppence to rub together.' He spread his hands. 'Well, what can we do? Now that he's dead, I suppose that's the end of it.'

Nelson spoke this time. 'I don't think we can say it's the end of it. Somebody must have been supplying him.'

Blair turned quickly towards the detective. 'How do you mean?'

'He wasn't in this on his own. It wasn't a little mickey mouse operation. There must have been others. How can we be sure they won't start up again?'

'Of course,' Blair said. 'You're right. We should look for the supplier.'

'Do you know someone called Baxter?' Megarry cut in. 'William Baxter? Name ring a bell? Does he live around here?'

Blair turned back to face Megarry. 'He's the local chemist.'

'Well then,' Megarry said. 'He's the supplier.'

'What?'

The police chief smiled, a cold parting of the lips with no trace of feeling in it. 'I have a print-out of Stewart's account. All the transactions. I know exactly where the money was going.'

'And Baxter's name is on it?'

'Yes,' Megarry said. 'Among others.'

The room fell silent. Megarry sat back in his chair and watched the inspector. After a while he spoke again. 'You know nothing about this? Nothing at all?'

'No, nothing. The whole thing is a total shock.'

Nobody spoke. Something was happening. The conversation was changing from a consultation into an interrogation.

'Tell me something,' Nelson suddenly said. 'That car out there. The Datsun. How can you afford that on your salary?'

Blair started to protest. He struggled to regain the moral ground. 'What sort of question is that?'

'It's a fair question,' Megarry said. 'Why don't you answer it?'

'Because it's personal. It's also hostile. I don't have to answer it.' He pushed the table away and tried to stand up.

Nelson put a hand on his shoulder and forced him back down. 'I'd like an answer.'

Blair's face had gone pale. 'I borrowed the money. What's that got to do with anything?'

'Can you tell us who from?'

Blair made another effort at defiance. He banged the table and the ashtray jumped. 'I don't have to put up with this. If Stewart was peddling angel dust, what's it got to do with me? Why am I being interrogated?'

Megarry didn't flinch. 'Because I think you might have been involved with him.'

Blair opened his mouth and for a moment no sound came out. 'That's preposterous.'

'Is it?'

The police chief reached into his pocket and took out the print-out. 'According to this, you were receiving regular payments from Stewart's account.' He bent to study the bundle of paper. 'Fifteenth December, 1989, cheque for five thousand pounds; 20 January, 1990, five thousand; 14 March, 1990, twelve thousand. Do you want me to go on?' Megarry waved the sheaf of papers. 'Altogether you got twenty-eight thousand pounds from him.' He leaned across the table till his face was almost touching Blair's. 'Now, why would he be so generous?'

'I can explain it,' Blair said.

'Well, then. Go ahead. We're listening.'

'Not here. Not in this hostile environment.'

Megarry slipped the print-out back in his pocket. 'Well, I'll tell you what I think. You set the whole thing up, didn't you? Isn't that what happened? You gave him the money to get started. But you kept well in the background. Baxter supplied him with the stuff and he went around selling it and lodging the proceeds in the bank account. Every so often, you siphoned off a nice little cheque. In effect, you ran the operation. At arms length, I think they call it.' He stopped. 'Have you got a bank account?'

Across Blair's pale forehead little beads of sweat stood like rain drops.

'I said have you got a bank account?'

'Yes.'

'I'd like to see it. We're also going to question Baxter. I think we can nail you.'

Blair had fallen silent.

'Stewart did molest that kid. The McClenaghan's were right about that. But you protected him. It was only when you couldn't avoid it that you finally brought him in for questioning. And even then you covered up for him. You pretended there was no case to answer and let him go.' Megarry sat back in the chair and caught his breath. His face was flushed. He looked at Blair and a feeling of loathing washed over him. 'I'm going to charge you. You know your rights. Do you want to ring your wife?'

Blair shook his head. 'I want a solicitor.'

# 14

Megarry opened a drawer and found the whiskey bottle.

'Here.'

He pushed the mug across to Nelson who took it reluctantly. 'What *is* this?'

'A celebration', Megarry said. 'We've uncovered a rotten apple. That calls for a drink.'

He lifted his own mug and downed the contents in one gulp, then quickly topped it up again. Nelson watched him with a growing sense of unease.

'You know, I never liked that bastard. From the first day I set eyes on him, I felt there was something wrong. Too much smarm. Too much friggin oil. Remember somebody alerted the BBC? It was him. For a miserable fifty-pound tip-off fee. He could have messed up the whole damned investigation. And then he goes and protects a friggin child molester.'

He screwed up his face in disgust.

'We should move these guys around. It isn't a good

idea to leave them alone for a long time in a small place like that. They learn bad habits. No one to keep an eye on them.'

He lifted the whiskey mug again.

'But we got him in the end,' Nelson said.

'Yeah we got him. But there are others. It's like a cancer. It spreads.'

He found his cigarettes and bent his head into the guttering match. 'It goes right to the top.'

Nelson didn't respond. He could see that a dark mood had descended on the police chief. The whole way from Glencraigie, Megarry had sat in the back of the car with Blair and hadn't said a word.

'You know, ever since I saw McCarthy lying in that car, I can't help feeling responsible. Look at the life he had. Scurrying from one sleazy bar to another, selling secrets, betraying his friends for a few lousy pounds. And then to end it all with a bag over his head on a lonely country road.'

'He knew what he was doing,' Nelson said. 'He knew the risks he took.'

'But I recruited him, for Christ's sake. I got him into this.' Megarry banged his fist on the table. 'I introduced him. Don't you think I bear some responsibility?'

'We couldn't operate without informers. They get well paid. They do it willingly.'

'No they don't. We bully them. We threaten them. We blackmail the poor fuckers. They're like rats caught in a trap, no way to turn. And then in the end, a bullet in the head. Maybe we don't pull the trigger but we do it to them just the same.'

He reached for the bottle again. Nelson could see that he was determined to get drunk.

'I never told you how I got into this racket, did I? It

was all an accident. Fate. The hand of God. I never set out to be a branchman.'

He poured another shot and Nelson waited.

'I was just a young rookie, fresh out of training school. One day the inspector came in looking for people to help out on a raid, so I volunteered. I thought it would be a bit of fun. That's how naive I was. They'd got word of an IRA meeting. Some big shots planning an operation. I was just a decoy, a very minor cog. We rushed the house and broke down the door and right inside there was a guy sitting on the stairs.

'I think he was a guard or something. I'll never forget the look on his face. He had a revolver between his hands and he just pulled the trigger. The whole thing seemed to take for ever, and when I looked round, the cop beside me had half his head blown away.'

'Jesus,' Nelson said.

'I suppose he saw himself as a soldier. Fighting for Ireland. How do we know how these guys feel? They used to top them in those days. I was the main prosecution witness. Three days in the box. He swung in the end. Guy called Morgan.

'A couple of weeks later, my father borrowed my car to go to a bowling tournament out at Glengormley. He'd only driven a couple of hundred yards when the car blew apart. It was a bomb. Meant for me.

'When it was all over, the Chief Constable called me in. He offered me a transfer to the Special Branch. I suppose they saw it as compensation for what I'd been through. I saw it as a chance to get revenge so I took it. I've spent my whole life conducting a vendetta. It's consumed me. And in the end what has been achieved?'

He looked at Nelson.

There was a look of pain in the young man's face.

'But you smashed the bastards. You locked them up. You put them out of business for a long time.'

Megarry was shaking his head.

'But they're back. Stronger than ever. It's like sowing dragon's teeth.'

'We have to keep trying. We have right on our side.'

'No,' Megarry said. 'It's not a question of right and wrong. We, too, have people who would think nothing of putting a gun to a man's head and blowing his brains out.'

'But there has to be an authority. A moral centre. That's what we are.'

Megarry lifted his drink. 'I'm not sure any more. I think we're all bound up in this thing together, us and the terrorists. Like Siamese twins. As if it was preordained and we had no control over it. Sometimes I think that the course is already set and nothing we do can alter it. We just play our parts to the bitter end.'

He lifted the whiskey bottle and screwed on the cap. Nelson reached out and held his arm.

'What are you going to do?'

'When it's over?'

'Yes.'

'I'm going to pack it in. I've had enough of it, John. All the intrigue, the blackmail, the interference. I feel contaminated. I think I'll go back to Kathleen. My daughter is sick. She needs me.'

'No,' Nelson said. 'You'll change your mind.'

'I don't think so.'

'And what about the case?'

'The case goes on. I think we're nearly there. Blair was just a side issue.'

'And Stewart? Why was he murdered?'

Megarry stubbed out his cigarette.

'Because he was in the wrong place at the wrong time.'

'I don't understand.'

'It had nothing to do with McCarthy. Nothing to do with Julie McClenaghan. It was an accident. He was murdered by accident.'

'So what was the connection between Stewart and McCarthy?'

'There wasn't one. Stewart was on his way to work. He just happened to arrive at Glencraigie crossroads when the killers were waiting for somebody else. He got murdered by mistake.'

'And McCarthy?'

'He was murdered because he knew too much. The same as Clarke. They were working as informers. They were killed to shut their mouths. By the same person. Using the same weapon.'

'And who was meant to die at Glencraigie instead of Stewart?'

'George O'Connor.'

Megarry suddenly pulled open a drawer.

'Let me show you something.'

He spread two pieces of paper on the flat desk-top.

'Do you see anything significant?'

'It's the same notepaper.'

'That's right.'

Megarry put the papers into his wallet.

'What are they?' Nelson asked.

'One of them is a note that McCarthy wrote to his girlfriend while he was away on one of his touting trips. She gave it to me when I went out to see her.'

'And the other one? It looks like a phone number.'

'It is,' Megarry said. 'It's the number of the killer.'

# 15

That morning he felt better than he had done for a long time. He knew it the moment he woke up; it was as if some problem had been solved, some long-postponed decision taken. It was the way he sometimes felt when a case came together and all the ends were neatly tied – a feeling of satisfaction, but tinged with disappointment, as if something he had long subscribed to had been shaken to its foundations.

As he fussed around the little flat preparing breakfast, he noticed again all the small details that had irritated him over the years, all the things he had meant to complain about and never got round to. The sad wallpaper with its imprint of dead flowers; the damp patch above the window where the condensation gathered in winter; the carpet scuffed and threadbare and in need of replacement from the first day he had moved in here.

He realised that he had never complained because he had never seen this room as permanent, only a temporary halting site on the journey home. He could feel no emotion for the place. It was somewhere to sleep, somewhere to wake up. He would leave it without regret, bequeath it to the next poor bugger who would take his place.

Likewise, the thought struck him that he should have done this a long time ago, packed it up and gone back. But he knew that to be false. Everything had its moment, its place in the order of things. And now the time was right.

He made a breakfast of cornflakes and toast. As he waited for the kettle to boil, he knocked the radio on and got a current affairs programme.

Someone was talking about the economy, in a cosy upbeat tone. The fundamentals were coming right: balance of payments, inflation, foreign debt. He caught the optimistic note in the voice and went to open the curtains.

The room was flooded in sunlight. As if on cue, the chatter on the radio stopped and someone was singing. *There's a bright golden haze on the meadow.* He let the curtains fall back and went to call Kathleen.

He listened to the phone ringing, picturing her putting the newspaper down and padding out into the hall. Or maybe she was already in the garden, tending the roses. She would have the french windows open and the sound would drift out to her. She would listen with a look of irritation, and then put the trowel down and rub her hands on her apron.

He could see her, as he had seen her so often in the past, walking quickly up the garden, anxious now to reach the phone in case the caller hung up.

'Hello.'

'Kathleen. It's me.'

'Where are you?'

He caught the surprise in her voice.

'I'm in the flat. I thought I'd give you a call. When were you thinking of going to the hospital?'

'This morning. Do you want to come?'

'I was going to go in the evening. I thought maybe we could meet. Go together.'

'That's no big problem. I can go again. She's glad of the company.'

'How about seven? Does that suit?'

'Seven's fine. Car park?'

'Sure.'

'Well then.'

He thought she was going to put the phone down. 'Wait,' he said. 'There's something else. I promised you dinner.'

'Don't worry about it.'

'We could go tonight. After the hospital.'

'You might be busy.'

'No. I'll be free. I'll make time.'

He heard her draw breath.

'Are you sure, Cecil? It can wait, you know.'

'I'm sure. I know a nice place. We need to talk.'

'You're not going to cancel? Nothing's going to come up to derail you?'

'Jeeesus,' Megarry said. 'I just told you. I'll be free. Why don't you believe me?'

He heard her start to laugh and felt his heart lift.

'I know you too well, Cecil.'

'Seven o'clock. In the car park?'

'All right,' she said.

He put the phone down and went into the bathroom and ran some hot water in the sink. As he selected a razor, he found himself humming. *Oh what a beautiful morning.*

He found Harvey in the canteen, eating a disgusting breakfast of egg and chips. He pulled over a chair and sat down beside him.

'Don't you care about yourself?' he said.

'What?'

'That goo. Do you know what that's doing to your arteries?'

Harvey stopped, a speared chip half-way to his mouth. 'For God's sake, Cecil. Are you lecturing me?'

'I'm telling you. That stuff is just dripping with cholesterol. Do you know the French won't eat more than two eggs a week?'

Harvey shook his head and started to smile. 'This is coming from *you*? The fittest man in the department. A man who doesn't drink. Doesn't smoke. Jogs every morning. Eats regular meals. Keeps his weight under control. Give me a break.' He reached for a steaming mug of tea.

'What did you hear about that arms theft?'

'There's nothing in it.'

'Nothing?'

'That's right. My guy knows nothing about it.'

'No chance of a mistake?'

'There's always a chance. You know that. But he says he never heard of it. I believe him. I don't think it happened.'

'That's what I thought,' Megarry said.


The office was empty. Megarry opened the windows to let in fresh air. He took his jacket off and checked the revolver in his shoulder holster, opening the chamber and counting the rounds.

He sat down and lifted the phone.

After a few moments a polite English voice came on the line.

'It's me. I thought I'd give you a buzz.'

Prescott perked up immediately.

'Superintendent. Good of you to call. I was thinking about you.'

'Well that's a coincidence.'

'How's the case?'

'Good. I've made a fair bit of progress, but I've hit a rock. I thought we should talk.'

'Of course. On the phone?'

'I don't think so,' Megarry said. 'Any chance we could meet?'

There was a slight hesitation.

'Look, I've a conference scheduled for ten minutes' time, and then I've a few other things. I can put them aside. What time do you make it?'

Megarry consulted his watch.

'Ten past ten.'

'I'll see you at eleven o'clock.'

'Fine. Will I come over?'

'I'll tell you what. I have to deliver some stuff. Why don't I meet you at the Castle Grounds. Do you know it?'

'Sure.'

'You can park your car. It's a nice morning. We could take a walk. Get some exercise.'

'Fine,' Megarry said.

He could hear Prescott chuckling.

'A bit of exercise will do you no harm. You could do with it.'

'Eleven o'clock,' Megarry said and put the phone down.

# 16

He watched him come slowly up the winding drive, through the copse and the trees at a leisurely pace, as if enjoying the scenery, the lough stretching like glass down below, and above the dark green canopy of Cave Hill.

Megarry waited till the sleek Mercedes had rounded into the car park and pulled up. He touched his breast pocket and then leaned forward to crush out his cigarette.

Prescott was alone, no driver. He stepped out of the car and stretched his arms, his tall physique every inch the soldier. He turned and sniffed the air and then spotted Megarry as he bent to lock his own car.

'Ah,' he said, walking towards him. 'You got here ahead of me. Magnificent view. You people don't realise what you have here.' He swept his arm out like a tourist guide extolling the local scenery. 'Woodlands, sea, mountains, all unspoilt. Why can't they just settle down and enjoy life without murdering each other? Look at that view.'

Megarry said nothing. In the bay a couple of yachts

scudded like moths across the still water. The Castlereagh Hills cast a dark shadow.

Prescott turned back to the police chief. 'You're so lucky, you know. Having all this on your doorstep. No, not on your doorstep, in the centre of the city almost. You should see some of the wastelands that pass for cities back in Britain.'

'But this is your home, too. You told me that, remember?'

Prescott smiled. 'But I'm not a native, not like you. I've no roots. That's what you told me.' He put his arm around Megarry's shoulder and drew him in a confidential embrace. 'You want to talk. Do you mind if we take a stroll?' He started to walk out through the deserted car park. Megarry fell in by his side. 'How's it going? You said you were making progress. Fleming hasn't bothered you again?'

'No. He seems to have backed off.'

'I had a little chat. Diplomatic. Along the lines I suggested. Smoothed the feathers down a bit. A lot of this has to do with ego, you know. Fighting for space, fighting for recognition. Psychiatrists think it goes all the way back to childhood. Poor parental encouragement, low self-esteem.'

Megarry was fumbling with his cigarettes again, puffing at a match. Prescott tut-tutted.

'You smoke too much. You should give them up. It's a very bad habit.'

'I know. People are forever telling me to stop smoking, stop drinking, take more exercise, but I feel all right. Most of the time, anyway. Today I feel excellent.'

'Well, that's good. How is the case? Tell me about it.'

They were walking along a path, slowly ascending the hill. Ahead the track was thinning and they would enter a wood.

'Did I tell you Stewart had a bank account with thirty-two thousand pounds in it? I know now where he got it.' Prescott was nodding. 'He was running a racket in angel dust. Well not running it, fronting for someone else, but that's where the money was coming from.'

'Angel dust?'

'Clenbuterol. It's a drug for fattening animals. It's illegal but apparently quite a few farmers use it.'

'I see.'

'He was a farm hand, a casual labourer. He worked the farms around Glencraigie, so he was ideally placed to peddle the stuff.'

'And he made thirty-two thousand?'

'More. I don't know the margins, but I suppose it was like any other drug. They were probably cutting it. He cleared almost seventy thousand in just over two years.'

'Well, that's not bad.' Prescott laughed. 'We're obviously in the wrong business. Who was he fronting for? Did you find out?'

Megarry blew out a wreath of smoke. 'Yes. Someone who should have known better. One of our own people, in fact.'

'Good Lord. Anyone I would know?'

'The local station inspector. Man called Blair. I think he rang you once.' Prescott looked up sharply. 'The morning of the murders. He tipped you off, remember? You told me you'd heard from the local man.'

'Ah yes. Decent type, I thought. Of course, I never met him. You must have been shocked.'

'Not really. I'd my doubts about him. In this business you learn not to be shocked. People can do the strangest things.'

'And was this related to the murder do you think?'

Megarry was shaking his head. 'I don't think so. I think it was probably an accident. The people who killed him were waiting for someone else. A man called George O'Connor.'

Prescott stopped. 'O'Connor? Where does he come in?'

'He's an old IRA veteran. Friend of John McCarthy. He used to be very active in the old days, but he's only on the fringes now. He's too old. Just like McCarthy was too old. The younger guys have taken over.'

Prescott rubbed his jaw. 'So you think they got the wrong man?'

'Afraid so. O'Connor was the man they were really after. McCarthy was supposed to set him up. Lure him out to Glencraigie on some pretext or other. But he didn't go. Stewart just happened to come along and got killed instead.' Megarry's face was perspiring. He stopped and wiped it with a handkerchief. 'It was around five am. I think Stewart was on his way to work. He started early.'

'And what about McCarthy? Did the same people kill him?'

'One of them did.'

'For what reason?'

Megarry made a shrugging gesture. 'His usefulness was at an end.'

'I don't follow,' Prescott said.

'He was touting. That's what all these little trips were about. He was working as an informer, travelling round the ghettoes in an unmarked car. Pointing out IRA sympathisers, safe houses, that sort of thing. He used to work in spells of a week or ten days. Then he'd come home. That way they could deflect suspicion.'

'How do you know this?'

'I put two and two together. He used to work for me years ago. He was very good. But recently I don't think he could have been up to much. The information he had would have been very low-grade stuff.'

Prescott leaned over and clapped him on the back. 'I must say you *have* made progress. Good for you. This'll shut them up at the next security meeting. Stop them nipping at your bum.' He laughed again and the sound echoed among the trees. 'There's something I don't understand. Why would they want to kill this man O'Connor? What had he done to offend them? You just said that he was on the fringes of the organisation. Was he informing, too?'

Megarry dropped his cigarette and ground it underfoot. They had climbed up into the wood. Below them, through the trees, he could see the castle and the car park. A couple of kids had appeared from somewhere and were running around, peering down over the battlements, playing some game or other.

'You're going too fast,' he said. 'There's more.'

Prescott's face spread in surprise.

'There was a man called Thomas Clarke. Milkman. Lived off the Springfield Road. He was killed in similar circumstances. I checked with his wife. He'd been doing the same routine as McCarthy. Disappearing for days on end. Coming home with money. Being a milkman, you see, he would know the ghettoes well and no one would suspect him.'

'And?'

'There's a link. They were murdered with the same weapon.'

'Browning?'

'Yes.'

'By God.' Prescott slapped his thigh.

'It had the barrel fixed so we couldn't identify the weapon.'

'Well, now, that's clever. Somebody who knew a bit about ballistics?'

'Obviously. There's something else. They were both working for a person called Barbarossa. Sounds like a cover-name. You know, like something a handler would use. A bit melodramatic, I think. They were only low-grade informers. Do you know what it means?'

'Of course. It was a plan Hitler had for the invasion of the Soviet Union.'

Megarry smiled. 'That was easy for you, wasn't it? You've a special interest in the war. Did you also know that Barbarossa was a Holy Roman Emperor and a Barbary pirate? There were several of them.'

Prescott turned and grinned. 'You've been boning up.'

'I checked it in the library. I think this person killed McCarthy and Clarke. Obviously had help with Stewart. An ambush, something like that. That would account for the different weapons. They were heavy calibre. A Kalashnikov and an Armalite.'

'You've certainly done your homework,' Prescott said. He looked at the police chief with a mixture of admiration and awe. 'All we need now is Barbarossa.'

Megarry suddenly stopped. He studied Prescott, the handsome face with the freckles round the nose, which he noticed now for the first time; the fine blond hair, the pale blue eyes, the curl of the lip. Could it be disdain, arrogance?

'Let me show you something.' He reached into his pocket and drew out two pieces of paper. 'Notice anything?'

Prescott scanned the notes but didn't speak.

'That was a note which McCarthy sent to his girlfriend when he was off on one of his trips. Do you recognise the other one?'

Prescott slowly raised his face. In his eyes, the arrogance had given way to something else.

'You gave me that note yourself. It's your direct line. You gave it to me after the security meeeting. Remember?'

Prescott started to say something but the police chief cut him short.

'You're Barbarossa, aren't you?'

The words sounded like a pistol shot. For a moment, Prescott's handsome face flushed with anger and then the muscles round his eyes relaxed and the arrogance returned. He threw his head back and laughed. 'You're crazy. You're stark raving mad.'

Megarry felt a dart of panic. 'Do you have a personal weapon?'

'Of course.'

'Browning?'

'This is ridiculous.'

Megarry persisted. 'Could I have it?'

Prescott reached inside his jacket and took out the gun. He started to hand it over and then seemed to change his mind.

'Don't,' Megarry said. In his own hand he held a small revolver. 'Just give it to me. Butt first.'

Slowly Prescott extended the gun. The police chief grabbed it and stuck it in his pocket.

'I have to arrest you. You know that.'

'Of course. You've got your job to do. That's fair enough.' He had regained some of his old confidence, talking now as if this was a polite conversation in an officer's mess. 'But no-one will believe you. It's all too fantastic. You'll ruin yourself.'

'We'll see,' Megarry said. 'I think you killed McCarthy and Clarke. I think you used this weapon. You were running your own operation. Freelancing. Running your own informers, and using the information you gathered to ingratiate yourself with the authorities. You were afraid that McCarthy or Clarke would spill the beans on you, so you just killed them.'

He paused.

'Isn't that so?'

The place had gone quiet. In the trees above them Megarry became aware of birds chattering in the branches. He hadn't heard it before. It was strange the things he had failed to notice.

'When I mentioned the Browning to you, you sold me a cock and bull story about a theft from an army base in North Antrim. It never happened. That was just to muddy the water.'

Prescott sniffed the air. 'Let's not waste time,' he said. 'We'd better be going.'

'I'm not finished,' Megarry said. 'You tried to kill O'Connor because McCarthy told you he was suspicious. He'd warned him. One old friend to another, so he became another mouth that had to be stopped. You told McCarthy to get him out to Glencraigie. But he was too cautious and didn't come, and Stewart got it instead.'

'Come on,' Prescott said, 'Let's be going.' He started to walk down the path, back towards the car park. Megarry followed, the pistol trained on his back.

'You can't go around killing people. This isn't Stalingrad. This isn't a game out of some military textbook. These are just ordinary people caught up in this bloody mess. You can't just kill them as if they had no worth. We're supposed to be above all that.' It seemed as if someone else was talking, the flow of conversation pouring out of him, like a child at confession. 'Why did you do it? Was it compensation? Was that it? You'd missed the big war so you made do with this miserable little scrap we have here. Was that it? And all that pallsy-wallsy stuff. Keep in touch with me. Let me help you. That was just so that you could keep tabs on the progress I was making.'

The blow caught Megarry in the midriff. He struggled to catch his breath and found his foot slipping on the loose earth.

Prescott hit him again below the neck and he began to go down, scratching desperately for something to hold on to.

There was a shot and the birds scattered. In the car park the kids stopped playing and looked up the hill towards the wood. A man appeared from somewhere and took a little boy's hand. 'It's all right,' he said. 'Just somebody shooting pigeons.'

# 17

There was a low rumble. Nelson looked up and saw the sky darken, a bank of cloud move in from the lough. It brought with it a gust of wind which shook the leaves of the elm trees near the cemetery gates and tossed the music sheets of the band, struggling with their instruments beside the open grave.

The crowd pressed forward and one or two people began to pull up their collars against the threatening rain. Up near the front, Nelson could see a small knot of dignitaries; the Secretary of State surrounded by nervous-looking security men, the Commander, the Chief Constable and a man with a mop of white hair who he took to be a prominent politician, although he couldn't remember his name.

Nelson searched the throng, looking for a face. Tall solemn men, bareheaded, and just a handful of women; mostly this was a male affair. Standing slightly apart from the rest he saw a thin figure in black. She stood with her hands before her, clutching a wreath of lilies, a light veil covering her face. As he watched, the Secretary bent to whisper something in her ear, consoling her, pressing her arm. Then he took his glasses off and wiped them with a handkerchief.

The band started, a few low notes and then the tuba swelling. *Abide With Me.* The crowd fell silent as the music drifted over the ranks of mourners, and out across the traffic moving fast along the motorway.

Nelson looked along the rows of tombstones, the weather-beaten crosses, the fading inscriptions, and thought of the last funeral he had attended and the words Megarry had used: Have you noticed how it always rains?

He felt a sadness take hold of him. Events had moved so quickly in the last forty-eight hours, overturning certainties, trailing confusion and change. Things would never be the same again.

The band had stopped playing. There was a brief pause and the words of the clergyman floated back across the bowed heads. 'The Kingdom of God is like a man setting off for a distant country who called together his servants and delivered to them his goods.' The parable of the talents. It was fairly predictable. He listened as the man spoke warmly of a life well-lived, the phrases slipping by in a low murmur. Ashes to ashes, dust to dust. There was another crash and the rain began to fall, big drops spattering his coat, splashing against his face. Here and there, black umbrellas were poking up towards the dull sky. Around the grave the crowd had started to break up, trying not to appear undignified but spurred on by the rain coming now in gusts. He found himself walking back towards the cemetery gates and the sanctuary of the car.

He heard a voice call his name and turned quickly. Megarry was beside him, his hands dug deep in the pockets of his gaberdine, a felt hat pulled down across his head. He felt a lump rising in his throat.

'You came. I didn't know whether you would.'

'Drysdale called me. Said it would look better.'

'So, how are you keeping?'

'So, so.'

'And what's going to happen?' The question was out before Nelson had time to think.

'There'll be an internal enquiry. I've been told to stay away until it's over.' He stopped and tried to light a cigarette, then gave up and began walking again. 'They want to say it was an accident.'

'And was it?'

'In a way, yes.'

At the gates, they stopped.

'So what's happening to you?' Megarry said.

'I've been reassigned. I'm working with Harvey now.'

Megarry nodded. 'You'll like Harvey. He's a professional. He knows his job.'

A small man in a black raincoat passed by and then turned for a moment and stared at them. Megarry met his gaze and the man lowered his eyes and walked quickly away.

'I'd better go,' Megarry said. 'Keep in touch.'

'Where can I contact you?'

'At Kathleen's house. I'll be there for a while.'

'Maybe we can have a beer sometime.'

'Yes,' Megarry said. 'I'd like that.'

He lowered his head into the wind and walked towards the line of parked cars, the rain dancing now in torrents and running into puddles on the rough ground.